Command Intent

COMMAND INTENT:
INTERNATIONAL PERSPECTIVES AND CHALLENGES

Edited by:
LCol Jeff Stouffer & Dr. Kelly Farley

CANADIAN DEFENCE ACADEMY PRESS

Canadian Defence Academy Press
PO Box 17000 Stn Forces
Kingston, Ontario   K7K 7B4

Produced for the Canadian Defence Academy Press
by 17 Wing Winnipeg Publishing Office.
WPO30349

Cover Photo: Provided by Canadian Forces Combat Camera

This document contains information authorized under the auspices of The Technical Cooperation Program (TTCP) for unlimited release and distribution. Any product or trademark identified in this document provides an example not a recommendation. *Command Intent: International Perspectives and Challenges* does not present the official policy of any participating nation organization. It consolidates the research literature on intent and identifies future research required to effectively apply this concept during contemporary operations. All organizations are invited to use the information it provides.

Library and Archives Canada Cataloguing in Publication

Command intent : international perspectives and challenges / edited by Jeff Stouffer & Kelly Farley.

Issued by: Canadian Defence Academy.
Produced for the Canadian Defence Academy Press by 17 Wing Winnipeg Publishing Office.
Includes bibliographical references and index.
ISBN 978-0-662-48295-6 (pbk)
Cat. no.: D2-224/2008E

1. Military art and science--Canada. 2. Canada--Armed Forces. 3. Operational art (Military science). 4. Command of troops. 5. Intention. I. Farley, Kelly M. J. (Kelly Matthew John), 1959- II. Stouffer, Jeff III. Canadian Defence Academy IV. Canada. Canadian Armed Forces. Wing, 17

U163.C45 2008   355.4'771   C2008-980115-6

Printed in Canada.

3 5 7 9 10 8 6 4 2

TABLE OF CONTENTS

Foreword   *Carol McCann and Ross Pigeau* i

Preface   *Colonel Bernd Horn* v

Chapter 1   Commander's Intent: The Key to Success in the Contemporary Environment
Colonel Bernd Horn 1

Chapter 2   Common Intent as a Theoretical Construct
David J. Bryant, Ann-Renée Blais and Joseph V. Baranski 15

Chapter 3   Judging Intention: Integrating Insights from Cognitive Science and Neuroscience
Oshin Vartanian 45

Chapter 4   Fostering Trust within Network-Enabled Operations: Challenges and Initial Recommendations
Sandra C. Hughes and Joan H. Johnston 67

Chapter 5   Measurement of Intent: A Selective Review of the Literature
Keith Stewart 87

Chapter 6   Designing Net-Centric Interfaces to Capture Commander's Intent
Brian P. Donnelly and Scott M. Galster 105

Contributors 139

Glossary 143

Index 147

FOREWORD

Our interest in command intent began in a roundabout way in 1994 when we asked – perhaps naively – the simple question: "What is the state of command and control science?" At that time, our assessment was that command and control (C2) research seemed almost exclusively devoted to developing better information and communication systems, with little or no effort being directed towards analyzing the phenomenon of C2 itself. Intuitively, we felt that something was missing. We therefore immersed ourselves in a year-long engagement with junior and senior commanders from all three military services in Canada, and internationally, in an effort to find the essence (key attributes?) of command. The experience was exhausting but revealing, giving us a newfound respect for the commitment, sensitivity and professionalism of military commanders. We concluded that although commanders viewed C2 systems (i.e., technology) positively, the importance of these systems in the successful achievement of their missions was relatively low. More important, in these commanders' opinions, were the skills of leadership and motivation, of handling stress, making insights, taking responsibility, being accountable, promoting teamwork, resolving conflict, engendering trust, maintaining perspective, delegating authority, etc. In short, they viewed command first and foremost as a complex human skill that was indispensable for dealing with the types of complex human conflict that they would inevitably face. We concluded that command and control science needed to include research into such notoriously difficult areas as creativity, emotion, pattern recognition, empathy, social interaction, influence, trust and, above all, intent. This spawned the *Human in Command* research program and thus originated our enduring interest in intent.

As we discovered, commanders regard the correct formulation and articulation of intent as indispensable for mission success. In hindsight, this discovery now seems unremarkable. For those military members who hold (or have held) command positions, especially under difficult operational conditions, the importance of intent, command intent, common intent, and even adversarial intent, is glaringly obvious, even axiomatic. "How else" they legitimately ask, "could I possibly coordinate the efforts of my subordinates or, as importantly, interpret the actions of my enemies without both being able to impart my own intent or to infer the intent of others?" To commanders, the importance of intent is so self-evident that they rarely question its relevance. Rather, their questions revolve around how they can establish intent properly, or how they can propagate it effectively, or how they can be sure that their intent has been inferred correctly. In short, their focus is on the *practice* of establishing intent, not on its purpose or importance.

Unfortunately, the situation is not as straightforward for scientists. We have the more fundamental challenge of articulating precisely what the concept entails and implies. For instance, what, exactly, does the concept of intent mean? Does intent have a psychological basis – i.e., is the unit of inquiry the individual person? Or is intent best described as a sociological phenomenon – i.e., is the unit of inquiry at the group level? What are its defining characteristics? Why, specifically, is intent so important to commanders? Is command intent measurable, or can it only be qualitatively described? Cognitively, how do commanders create intent and further, how does it get shared? How do they know whether their intent was interpreted correctly by others? What are the telltale signs of poorly understood intent? Scientific answers to such questions will provide crucial knowledge for commanders. Such answers will also assist military organizations in developing policies and programs for ensuring that future commanders are properly trained in the formulation of intent, thereby reducing the likelihood that ambiguous or contradictory intent will be promulgated.

We applaud the editors of and contributors to this volume for bringing together some of the most recent scientific thinking on intent. It is time that the scientific community gave the topic the full attention that it truly deserves. We caution the reader, however, not to expect definitive insights or decisive conclusions: intent is one of the most difficult psychological concepts to study. In our experience, understanding intent requires that some of the most profound aspects of human psychology be addressed. What roles do chance and necessity, human volition and will, perception and reality, truth and deceit play in the formulation of intent? Difficult questions, not for the faint of heart, but questions that need to be asked and answered nonetheless. Advances in the understanding of intent will require contributions from the fields of motivation and emotion, decision making, knowledge representation, communications and social cognition. The contributions in this book are an important start and we look forward to more such efforts.

Ross Pigeau, PhD
Carol McCann, MASc
Defence Research and Development Canada – Toronto

PREFACE

I am very pleased to introduce *Command Intent: International Perspectives and Challenges*, the latest multinational volume published by CDA Press. This publication is of special significance and importance as it continues the deep-seated tradition of international research cooperation in military affairs that dates back at least to 1957, when the President of the United States and the Prime Minister of Great Britain issued a joint *Declaration of Common Purpose* that stated in part:

> The arrangements which the nations of the free world have made for collective defense and mutual help are based on the recognition that the concept of national self sufficiency is now out of date. The countries of the free world are interdependent and only in genuine partnership, by combining their resources and sharing tasks in many fields, can progress and safety be found. For our part we have agreed that our two countries will henceforth act in accordance with this principle.[1]

The result of this ambitious partnership became the Tripartite Technical Cooperation Program, later renamed The Technical Cooperation Program (TTCP), which is an international organization comprised of representatives from Australia, Canada, New Zealand, the United Kingdom and the United States. Significantly, it promotes defence research program harmonization and alignment in a collegial spirit of interdependence.

This publication represents the continuing effort of the broader international military research community to further collective understanding of time-proven and emerging military concepts. Standing in testament to the power of common purpose, this volume demonstrates clearly what can be accomplished when the marked abilities of a diverse group of international research agencies are pooled. It also reinforces, of course, the growing interest in and value of information sharing and how such efforts can truly serve as catalysts for the development of joint research initiatives.

This informative book not only brings together what we currently know about intent, but also approaches the subject from a variety of perspectives, including amongst them the technological, the psychological and the sociological. I am certain that the reader will come to better appreciate the complexity surrounding command intent and what this concept means for military forces as they grapple with the challenges inherent in the contemporary operating environment. Although it is largely research-oriented and theoretical in scope, I am confident that this volume will promote lively discussion and debate. One of its main strengths, however, is that it identifies the future research necessary to better understand and effectively apply this concept during operations.

Much work remains to be done if we are to truly appreciate command intent and use it to our advantage, yet this short volume is certainly a step in the right direction, and a significant step at that. Further research will undoubtedly be the result, and should this be so, then this book will have served an invaluable purpose.

Command Intent: International Perspectives and Challenges is a significant accomplishment of Technical Panel 11 (TP11), an element of the Human Resources and Performance Group within TTCP that provides the defence agencies of the five participating nations with advice and guidance on the psychological and social-psychological aspects of command such as the sharing of intent and leadership dynamics. Its members, and especially those authors that contributed to this volume, must be commended for their efforts in moving this and other undertakings from the merely possible to the actual. Should you wish to discuss any issues, research or opinions as presented in this book, TTCP TP11 or the Canadian Defence Academy would be pleased to entertain your inquiries.

Colonel Bernd Horn, Chairman, Canadian Defence Academy Press

---

1   See http://www.dtic.mil/ttcp/overview.htm, accessed 18 January 2008.

CHAPTER 1

Commander's Intent: The Key to Success in the Contemporary Environment

Colonel Bernd Horn

INTRODUCTION

Canada has been involved in Afghanistan for four and half years. The last two years have been particularly difficult and hazardous. The global community's attempts at rebuilding Afghanistan from a failed state to a vibrant, democratic country have not been without challenge. Notably, the Canadian campaign with its three-pronged approach of governance, reconstruction and security has been difficult to implement in the midst of a foreign culture, a corrupt governance structure, and a complex coalition design, not to mention a rampant insurgency.

Nonetheless, the military must work within this complex framework. For commanders and soldiers, fighting the enemy is not enough. Although Afghanistan is case specific, the characteristics and attributes of the counter-insurgency and particularly the issues of rebuilding a failed state and all that that implies are representative of the challenges that commanders and leaders will face in the contemporary operating environment. As such, the reliance on situation- or task-specific direction and orders is no longer a viable option. Those operating in the field who are charged with linking tactical successes in order to accomplish operational goals, which in turn lead to strategic success, require the agility and flexibility to adapt to circumstances and situations on the ground and on the fly. Therefore, they require the trust and empowerment of their seniors to get the job done. Their actions, however, must be in line with the larger goals of the organization so that the necessary

1

linkage of tactical actions to operational and strategic goals can be achieved. In other words, their actions must be linked to the commander's intent, the key to success in the contemporary operating environment.

THE CONTEMPORARY OPERATING ENVIRONMENT

The ambiguous, dynamic, fluid, multi-faceted and often combative nature of the contemporary operating environment has spawned a reliance on an entirely new concept of operations for armies that for decades have trained to fight a very limited, choreographed conflict between symmetrical opponents. In the contemporary environment, military forces are required to conduct humanitarian, peacekeeping and warfighting operations, potentially all on the same day, and all within the same geographic area.

Moreover, although many threats are geographically confined, international terrorist networks (e.g., al-Qaeda) pose a global threat. Quite simply, their goals, operational methodologies and adaptability have shifted the nature of trans-national insurgencies. They employ asymmetric strategies in attacks following a doctrine of propaganda by deeds. They use the tactics of terrorism and guerrilla warfare in the pursuit of their objectives and have refined other disruptive techniques including suicide bombings, improvised explosive devices and mass casualty events. Additionally, they exploit globalization (e.g., telecommunications, financing, internet interconnectivity for information operations, and sharing of both lessons learned and techniques, tactics and procedures). In addition, the proliferation of technology continues to enhance their capacity and reach. These organizations are networked, multi-layered and complex entities capable of detailed operational planning, synchronization and execution. The enemy that we face, described Major-General Robert Scales, "is dedicated to tactics, techniques and procedures (TTPs) that are unacceptable to western nations; they are organized and networked; passionate and fanatical; committed; relentless and savage."[1]

Moreover, they practice Fourth Generation Warfare (4GW),[2] a concept in which the enemy uses largely asymmetric tactics[3] to achieve their aim; where human (non-kinetic) not technological solutions are paramount; and where integrated operations in a long war scenario provide the best hope for success (i.e., cooperation and coordination between all players: joint (all four services in the military); law enforcement agencies; other government departments; coalition partners; allies; national and international agencies).

In the current security environment, militaries need soldiers, leaders and commanders with judgment, wisdom and reasoning abilities, not just technical skills. Increasingly, we find that we are unwilling or unable to bring our technological superiority to bear. "You're going to have people coming at you who don't play by the rules," observed Harvard University political scientist Michael Ignatieff, "and you're going to have people coming at you who have an infinitely greater willingness to risk anything, i.e., their lives, than you may and that's one of the challenges you have to face."[4]

In essence, the current security operating environment is chaotic, volatile, uncertain and ever-changing. The ambiguous nature and asymmetric conditions inherent in most conflicts today require militaries to rapidly deploy forces that can apply special skills sets in a variety of environments and circumstances to achieve difficult missions in peace, conflict or war. One veteran commander observed, "For the soldier on the ground the environment is quite simply a sea of complexity."[5] Although excellent equipment may provide a technological edge, deployed forces must ensure that they are composed of leaders and soldiers who are adaptive and agile.

Importantly, leaders and their followers must be able to transition through the entire spectrum of conflict seamlessly. Colonel Roger Noble, the commander of the Al Muthanna Task Group in Iraq from April to November 2005, stated, "Situations develop rapidly, change constantly and demand situationally specific reactions." He added, "Problems are never purely military specific or tactical – [they are a] mixture of social, cultural, legal, moral and political." He concluded, "Success relies on shaping and influencing outcomes and then quickly adapting and exploiting to the actual outcomes. War among the people [i.e., insurgencies] requires those face to face with the people to have the will, means, authority and freedom to act to achieve the mission."[6]

MISSION COMMAND

In essence, although highly touted for years in theory as the operating concept within the Canadian Army, although not necessarily demonstrated in practice, mission command has become essential because of the nature of the environment under which the military must now operate. Mission command is a command philosophy that promotes decentralized and timely decision-making, freedom and speed of action, and initiative that is responsive to superior direction.[7] It entails three enduring tenets: the importance of understanding a superior commander's intent; a clear responsibility to fulfil that intent; and timely decision-making. At its core, the fundamentals of mission command are: unity of effort; decentralized authority; trust; mutual understanding; and timely and effective decision-making.

Simply put, mission command entails commanders issuing their orders in a clear and detailed manner that ensures their subordinates fully understand the larger intent, their specific assigned missions, as well as the significance of their own missions within the context of the larger plan/framework. In sum, subordinates are given the effect that they are to achieve and the reason why they must achieve it. Importantly, subordinates are also allocated the appropriate resources to achieve success. Commanders should impose a minimum of control measures to ensure that they do not unnecessarily limit the initiative or freedom of action of their subordinates. This allows the latter to decide within their respective freedoms of action how best to achieve their assigned mission.

It must be understood that mission command is situational. It does not apply to all people or all situations. While micro-management and/or rigid, superfluous direction may cause resentment and stagnation of both creativity and initiative, a lack of direction can produce little effect, or in fact, a negative effect. Subordinates must be well-trained and possess the ability and skill to be able to execute decentralized tasks. Junior, inexperienced individuals, or subordinates provided by some coalition forces, may not be capable of exercising mission command due to their lack of training, knowledge and/or experience. Equally, some situations that demand decisive and quick action, such as immediate crises, may also not lend themselves to mission command.

COMMANDER'S INTENT

Within mission command, and particularly within the context of the contemporary operating environment, the commander's intent becomes the critical component of mission success. The commander's entire effort (as well as that of his or her staff and subordinates) whether in planning, directing, allocating resources, supervising, motivating, and/or leading, is driven and governed by the commander's vision, goal or mission and the will to realize or attain that vision, goal or mission. The commander's intent is the commander's personal expression of why an operation is being conducted and what is to be achieved. It is a clear and concise statement of the desired end-state and acceptable risk. Its strength is the fact that it allows subordinates to exercise initiative in the absence of orders, or when unexpected opportunities arise, or when the original concept of operations no longer applies. "Decentralized and sophisticated methods, reliant on adapting to circumstance," noted one veteran commander, "require a binding 'glue' to ensure that action taken is coherent and directed towards a common end."[8]

As such, within the framework of mission command, subordinates have the latitude to exercise judgment, discretion and, most important, to act based on the situation and circumstances that they actually face on the ground. Not restrained by limiting direction or orders, and empowered to make decisions in the absence of the same, subordinates can continually achieve results by taking advantage of opportunities as they arise and minimize damage as situations change. In essence, the ability to make timely decisions equates to a larger number of positive options available to react to, or pre-empt, events.

For example, in August 1994, during Operation Lance, the Canadian commander of the UN Assistance Mission for Rwanda (UNAMIR II) received reports of mass killings in the southeast region of the country in the area designated "Sector 2 Bravo." Short of troops, he dispatched 8 Platoon of 3 Commando from the Canadian Airborne Regiment to the region with the simple directive to provide a presence in order to increase the population's confidence and to confirm the veracity of the stories.[9] Fully apprised of the commander's intent, the airborne soldiers developed a plan by which they would create a presence that masked their actual small size. Through a continuous and aggressive vehicle and foot patrol regimen, they seemingly flooded the area with their presence. Their success was such that the UNAMIR II commander wrote:

> The local government and military commanders were convinced that the Canadians had deployed at least one and perhaps two companies into the sector. Most of the villages in the sector were deserted at the beginning. After constant patrolling of all villages, the people gained confidence in the level of security afforded them and started to return.

Based on the clear understanding of the commander's intent, less than 40 soldiers were able to transform a near crisis situation into a success. In less than a month, they filled a security vacuum, created an impression of strength and presence, and imbued confidence in the local population. In short, they achieved the commander's operational requirement. Amazingly, at the end of the three week period, they were replaced by an entire infantry battalion.[10]

However, the intent must be articulated, explained and updated regularly. Commanders should never assume that their intent as dictated once in orders will translate into clear direction throughout the chain of command. As always, communications, one of the most vital components of military operations, is also arguably one of the weakest areas whether in garrison or on operations. Even face-to-face discussions carry the risk of misinterpretation, unwanted nuances and failed comprehension of key messages or content.

For example, in the aftermath of the 11 September 2001 (9/11) terrorist attack on the World Trade Center in New York City, the decision-making structure of Canada and of the Department of National Defence descended into seeming paralysis as political leaders and commanders desperately tried to glean some clarity as to ongoing events. At the unit level, we were given a stand-by/get ready to move order. Ambiguity understandably reigned and it was difficult to determine what was required. I therefore decided to do what I could to eliminate this ambiguity in the interest of my troops. As such, as a commanding officer, I gave a detailed set of orders to my company commanders and key battalion staff. I tried to explain the situation as best we knew it. I spelled out my intent to provide as much clarity and direction as possible on how we would prepare to meet any and all tasks. Notably, I expressed the importance of communications, keeping everyone as up to date as possible with events (we went so far as to have large televisions set up in the drill hall so people could watch CNN, the only source of information we received). Moreover, I spelled out the situation as best we knew it; notice to move timelines; and probable tasks and probable locations so that the sub-units could load their vehicles accordingly and have their soldiers pack their kit.

At the end of the orders I felt good. I believed that my intent was clear and I had now taken away the ambiguity. Months later, however, I had the occasion to see the orders that were issued by one of the platoon commanders to his section commanders, who in turn were to transmit them to the troops. The platoon commander received my intent and orders from his company commander who attended my orders group. The platoon commander's direction was filtered down to three lines – no idea what's happening; be prepared to move; could be anywhere to do security-type tasks. Hardly the intent I had given or hoped would have been passed to the troops.

To be successful, commander's intent must be clear, succinct and reinforced. It must be an issue of constant discussion at all levels. Commanders must personally take responsibility for continually revisiting and reinforcing their intent. Every possible venue must be utilized. For example, commander's intent should be covered during visits to units, sub-units or detachments; during "commander's hour;" and it should be built into training, exercises and professional development. It can be wargamed or simply discussed. In the end, the more complex the environment in which individuals operate, the more imperative it is that they fully understand the commander's intent so that they can effectively translate their decisions and actions into useful tactical gains that accomplish the larger mission.

Equally, for commander's intent to be effective, there must be unity of command, which requires a single, clearly identified commander that is appointed for any given operation and who is accountable to only one superior. This ensures clarity and promotes unity of effort, promotes timely and effective decision-making, and avoids conflict in orders and instructions. It is characterized by a clear chain of command, where command at each level is focused on one commander.

Command climate is another important ingredient to the successful imposition of mission command and the effectiveness of the concept of commander's intent. Normally, commanders exercise command through the force of their personality and leadership to influence the attitude, direction and motivation of the staff and subordinate commanders. A commander's ability to create an effective and positive command climate has a direct impact on the morale and level of performance of the personnel within the organization. Positive leadership, sincerity and compassion by the commander stimulates subordinate confidence, enthusiasm, mutual trust and teamwork. In addition, encouragement to think independently, use initiative and accept risk, as well as inclusion of staff and subordinates in the decision-making process, all assist in creating an effective command climate.

For mission command to be successful, the command climate must encourage subordinate commanders at all levels to think independently, take the initiative, and not be risk averse. After all, the strength of mission command is the ability of commanders at all levels to react quickly to developing situations in an ambiguous, complex, fluid and chaotic operational environment. In such a context, it is critical to gain and maintain the initiative. Delay in decision-making can have serious consequences. As a result, subordinate commanders, acting within the commander's intent, must make decisions and take action.

For this chain of events to occur, trust is required. The superior commander must trust his subordinates to act, to act in accordance with the commander's intent, and to make reasonable decisions regardless of the circumstances the subordinate commander finds himself/herself in (which in an ambiguous and chaotic security environment may not necessarily be those the superior commander originally envisaged). This trust is critical, since for mission command to function, the superior must minimize control mechanisms and allow subordinates the necessary freedom of action and initiative to achieve the necessary effect.

Similarly, subordinates must have confidence that they have not been given an unachievable task. They must also trust their superiors to provide the necessary direction, guidance and resources to successfully achieve the assigned mission. For subordinates to fully exercise initiative and accept the necessary degree of risk, they must be able to trust their superior to provide the necessary support should errors (i.e., neither malicious, nor due to negligence) occur. Without question, an accountability framework must exist. Quite simply, people must be held accountable for their actions. However, equally vital, it must be made clear that honest mistakes are acceptable. Mistakes, noted one veteran commander, "must not be seen as an action that generates an adverse or negative result."[11]

SUMMARY

In the end, the current ambiguous, chaotic and volatile operating environment requires agility of thought and action. Subordinates cannot be encumbered with clumsy, restricted, or time-consuming command processes that do not allow them to react instantly in an appropriate manner. However, their actions must be guided to ensure that tactical success on the ground leads to operational and strategic success. As such, the concept of mission command, specifically with its fundamental component of the commander's intent, provides the mechanism that provides the necessary vision, direction and purpose to subordinates so they can accomplish their assigned missions. Through this mechanism, decentralized and timely decision-making, freedom and speed of action, and initiative that are all responsive to superior direction, enable success.

ENDNOTES

1   Major-General Robert Scales, presentation at "Cognitive Dominance Workshop," West Point, 11 July 2006. This new era of conflict has also spawned a new threat even within Western nations, namely the radicalization of elements within the society of developed nations – homegrown terrorists. Recent examples include the UK "shoebomber" (i.e., an attempt to destroy an aircraft with a bomb hidden in the sole of a running shoe), the terrorists who conducted the London subway

bombing, and the "Toronto 17," a group of Canadian homegrown terrorists who established a training camp in Ontario, Canada.

2   The concept of 3BW dominated during the 1990s as a result of the context of the times. Failed and failing states, such as Somalia and the former Yugoslavia, fixated UN and Western efforts. Nonetheless, as early as October 1989, former Lieutenant-Colonel William S. Lind had introduced the concept of 4GW in the *Marine Corps Gazette*. Although overshadowed by other theorists at the time, his idea gained prominence after 9/11. According to Lind, first generation warfare was characterized by linearity and order, an environment where states held a monopoly on the use of war to obtain political ends. The next generation of war, 2GW, was ushered in by the First World War. It was a function of fire and movement captured in the mantra "artillery conquers, infantry occupies." 3GW was also introduced during this war by German storm-troopers, but was refined and became dominant during the Second World War where it was showcased by German blitzkrieg tactics. In simplest terms, 3GW was manoeuvre warfare. 4GW refers to a non-linear, asymmetric approach to war in which agility, decentralization and initiative are instrumental to success. Antagonists utilizing 4GW normally favour indirect and asymmetric approaches, however, they will employ the full range of military and other capabilities in order to erode an adversary's power, influence and will. In essence, 4GW "seeks to convince the enemy's political decision makers/political leaders that their strategic goals are either unachievable or too costly for perceived benefit." The struggle "is rooted in the fundamental precept that superior political will, when properly employed, can defeat greater economic and military power." It is fought across the entire spectrum of society and human activity – political, military, economic, social. In short, 4GW is intended to influence and affect the non-military population of a nation. It is, as General Sir Rupert Smith asserts, "war amongst the people." Its use is meant to collapse an enemy internally versus destroying them physically. Furthermore, 4GW departs radically from the traditional model in which the conduct of war was the monopoly of states. It evolved out of the radically different conditions of the post-Cold War era. It is not a type of war for conquest or territory. The enemy is not a nation-state and its people. Rather, in 4GW, non-state actors such as Hamas, al-Qaeda and the Taliban become serious opponents, capable of operations outside of their traditional areas of operation. Moreover, in 4GW, the definition of combatants diverges significantly from the traditional laws of armed conflict. 4GW is non-linear, widely dispersed and largely undefined. It has few, if any, definable battlefields and the difference between "civilian" and "military" is often indistinguishable. The concept of 4GW is not without criticism. Some analysts have stated that 4GW is so vague and all-encompassing that it can include everything and as a result is of little value. However, it does provide a construct by which to examine asymmetric tactics and evolution of warfare. Moreover, placed in

the context of ongoing conflicts, it also provides a framework to understand enemy intent and TTPs, as well as to prepare one's own forces. See William S. Lind, "The Changing Face of War: Into the Fourth Generation," *Marine Corps Gazette* (October 1989), 22-26; Thomas X. Hammes, "Modern Warfare Evolves Into a Fourth Generation," *Unrestricted Warfare Symposium 2006 Proceedings*, 65; and General Sir Rupert Smith, *The Utility of Force: The Art of War in the Modern World* (London: Allen Lane, 2005), xiii.

3   Asymmetry, according to American strategist Steven Metz, "is acting, organizing and thinking differently from opponents in order to maximize one's own advantages, exploit an opponent's weaknesses, attain the initiative, or gain greater freedom of action." He adds, "It can entail different methods, technologies, values, organizations, time perspectives, or some combination of these ... [and it] can have both psychological and physical dimensions." Doctrinally, an asymmetric threat is a concept "used to describe attempts to circumvent or undermine an opponent's strengths while exploiting his weaknesses, using methods that differ significantly from the opponent's usual mode of operations." At its core, asymmetry is not designed to win battlefield victory. Rather, its aim is to disrupt, distract and disconnect. In short, to wear down a normally superior opponent. "Difficult to respond to in a discriminate and proportionate manner," explained strategist Colin Gray, "it is of the nature of asymmetric threats that they are apt to pose a level-of-response dilemma to the victim. The military response readily available tends to be unduly heavy-handed, if not plainly irrelevant, while the policy hunt for the carefully measured and precisely targeted reply all too easily can be ensnared in a lengthy political process which inhibits any real action." See Steven Metz and Douglas V. Johnson II, "Asymmetry and US Military Strategy: Definition, Background, and Strategic Concepts," US Army War College, Strategic Studies Institute, January 2001, 5-6; Colonel W.J. Fulton, DNBCD, "Capabilities Required of DND, Asymmetric Threats and Weapons of Mass Destruction," Fourth Draft, 18 March 2001, 2/22; and Colin Gray, "Thinking Asymmetrically in Times of Terror," *Parameters* 32, 1 (Spring 2002), 6.

4   Michael Ignatieff, *Virtual War: Ethical Challenges* (Annapolis: United States Naval Academy, March 2001), 8.

5   Colonel Roger Noble, "The Essential Thing: Mission Command and its Practical Application," *Australian Defence College Command Papers* 1 (2007), 7.

6   Ibid.

7   Command is the vested authority that an individual lawfully exercises over subordinates by virtue of their rank and assignment. It is the purposeful exercise

of authority over structures, resources, people and activities. The NATO accepted definition, which has been adopted by Canada, defines command as "the authority vested in an individual of the armed forces for the direction, co-ordination, and control of military forces." Canada, *Command* (Ottawa: DND, 1997), 4.

8   Noble, "The Essential Thing," 9.

9   8 Platoon, 3 Commando, was deployed to Rwanda as the Security and Protection Platoon for 1 Canadian Division Headquarters and Signals Regiment as part of Operation Lance.

10   See Bernd Horn, *Bastard Sons: An Examination of Canada's Airborne Experience 1942-1995* (St. Catharines: Vanwell Publishing, 2001), 225-226.

11   Noble, "The Essential Thing," 11.

CHAPTER 2

Common Intent as a Theoretical Construct

David J. Bryant, Ann-Renée Blais and Joseph V. Baranski

DEFENCE RESEARCH AND DEVELOPMENT CANADA – TORONTO

BACKGROUND

Recent coalition operations (e.g., Iraq, Afghanistan and Darfur) have highlighted the potential range and complexity of contemporary military missions. Despite the faster pace and greater uncertainty of these "complex endeavours,"[1] there appears to be an emerging consensus among Western military organizations as to the major approaches to conflict resolution in the foreseeable future. In particular, certain nations are adopting the concepts of Network-Enabled, Integrated and Effects-Based approaches to operations as drivers for the development of new policy, doctrine and training.

Network-Enabled Operations (NEOps) has recently emerged among The Technical Cooperation Panel (TTCP) nations (Canada, the United States, the United Kingdom, Australia and New Zealand) as the favoured term to refer to distributed operations, as they are broadly defined. NEOps shares elements with the earlier concept of Network-Centric Warfare (NCW),[2] but it encompasses a broader range of applications and capabilities, as well as a greater emphasis on the human dimensions (cognitive, social and organizational) than the technological.[3]

Recent operations are not only more complex, but they also involve a broader range of active players. Few, if any, future operations will be entered into unilaterally and they will inevitably involve collaboration among coalition partners, Other Government Departments

(OGDs), and various Non-Governmental Organizations (NGOs). As a result, the concept of integrated operations has become prominent as a framework in which to consider how distinct agencies might work together. In the Canadian context, for example, this trend is reflected in the development of supporting concepts, such as Joint, Interagency, Multinational, Public (JIMP),[4] 3D (Defence, Development and Diplomacy) or, more generally, the so-called "Whole of Government Approach" to operations.[5]

Although the origins of the Effects-Based Approach to Operations (EBAO) has its historical roots in U.S. Air Force doctrine,[6] the concept has more recently been expanded to encompass the leveraging of all kinetic and non-kinetic assets (e.g., political, economic, religious, social) to achieve a desired end-state.[7] EBAO is very complex because it requires an understanding of the intents of the relevant entities (i.e., coalition partners, NGOs, OGDs, adversaries and potential adversaries) and the inter-relationships among the myriad of variables that define, and are relevant to, the theatre of operations.[8]

The abovementioned concepts collectively define the conceptual underpinning for conducting 21st century operations. Importantly, a common feature of these concepts is the need for effective collaboration, often among distributed and diverse individuals, teams and organizations.[9] This reality underscores the critical importance of the human dimension of command and control (C2), which was defined by Ross Pigeau and Carol McCann, from Defence Research and Development Canada, as the "establishment of *common intent* to achieve coordinated action."[10]

Despite its resonance with military thinkers, the concept of common intent remains somewhat unclear. It is a psychological construct or theoretical set of cognitive processes and informational states that presumably underlies C2. But that presumption runs the risk of circularity – are we saying that common intent is essential to effective command and control because command and control is enhanced by common intent? To avoid such circularity of argument, we must independently define common intent as a theoretical entity and devise methods to measure and assess it. In so doing, we can then answer empirical questions about the role of common intent in command and control. In other words, we must establish the construct validity of common intent, that is, the extent to which the programs, doctrine and procedures we enact under the theory of common intent actually have observable effects that are predicted by the theory.

WHAT IS INTENT?

The first step in assessing the validity of common intent as a psychological construct is to define exactly what is meant by the term.[11] The topic of intent has always been of great interest to military organizations because every military operation needs direction – often a great deal of highly specific direction – and an objective, or desired end-state. The move towards network-enabled, integrated and effects-based operations has pushed this topic to the forefront once again.

A construct definition may vary in nature, ranging from a simple description to a well-defined conceptual framework involving hypothesized entities and processes.[12] The number of related observable variables and the specificity of their definitions vary greatly; obviously, the greater the number of observables, the more difficult it is to specify the conceptual framework.[13] Developing an instrument or a set of instruments to measure common intent thus implies sampling a domain with theoretically defined boundaries. The construct domain (i.e., the set of interrelated attributes that are included under a construct's label; a measuring instrument typically samples from this domain) should be defined with enough clarity so that researchers in the area can tell whether a particular component (e.g., item or task) fits within the definition. Furthermore, the domain should be defined as uni-dimensional or multi-dimensional, and the measuring instrument that is operationalizing the construct should reflect its dimensionality as well.[14] Domain definition encompasses the assessment of the internal consistency (i.e., this type of reliability estimate is concerned with whether all the items in a measuring instrument seem to be tapping the same underlying construct) of an assumed measure.[15] To the extent that the elements of a domain exhibit consistency, some construct may be employed to account for these interrelationships. Internal consistency, however, is a necessary, yet not a sufficient condition, for the validation of a construct.

COMMAND INTENT

It is with this idea of a theoretical construct in mind that we attempt to offer a definition of intent. There are several current uses of the term. The commander's intent – sometimes referred to as the commander's vision – captures the commander's overarching plan for an operation, its end-state, means and constraints. Whatever the level of command, the capability of the commander to articulate and promulgate his or her intent determines the success of the operation. Given the centrality of the commander's intent, military theorists and practitioners have extensively debated the best way in which intent should be formulated, communicated and implemented.

In practice, the commander's intent is formalized in a *statement of commander's intent.* Although there are variations among different military organizations, the commander's intent statement is usually composed of purpose, method (or tasks) and desired end-state, with a strong emphasis on brevity and clarity. The emphasis is on the ends rather than the means, but it is meant to enhance the synchronization of units. Indeed, the usefulness of including any statement of method has been questioned on the grounds that it could detract from the clear specification of goals and inhibit initiative on the part of subordinate commanders.[16] Nevertheless, the format and place of the intent statement in written or formal orders tend to be standardized within an organization across unit levels.[17] The level of detail to which the statement of intent is written tends to be a function of the kind of orders promulgated and the time available.

The usefulness of the commander's statement of intent stems not only from the actual statement that is disseminated, but also from the process of formulating the statement itself during planning. As an explicit mission-related statement, subordinate commanders and their planning teams use it as a point of reference for developing their own statement of intent, for planning their own mission, and in action during execution of the mission, especially when original plans falter. It is at this stage that the commander and staff frame the operational problem, define assets, constraints, the environment and so on. By framing the problem, the commander can create a shareable mental model for the operation that is more useful than a mere set of directives. Thus, the statement of intent should allow subordinate commanders to make decisions that are consistent with the framework devised by the commander.[18]

Command intent has gained significance through the development of advanced theories of command. Mission command, for example, emphasizes command based on sharing intent. By establishing common intent within the command and control organization, decision-makers are better able to make decisions in line with the intent of higher commanders and make those decisions more quickly than they might otherwise have. This fact is key to EBAO, in which the commander attempts to specify operational goals as well as the causal reasoning behind the plan. Because the emphasis is on the functional implication of actions (i.e., what effects they will have) and not the actions themselves, planners can convey the intent of the operation more effectively. This helps decision-makers understand *why* a course of action has been adopted and how they can contribute to achieving the desired effect.

Similarly, NEOps places importance on effective sharing of command intent, not just as specific tasks, but also as a conceptual model of how the commander sees the operation evolving and playing out over time. To achieve greater operational tempo and more effective performance of operations, NEOps requires the use of highly integrated, networked systems of people, technology, information and doctrine. It assumes that extensive sharing of information will allow physically distributed forces to "self-synchronize" and act in a coordinated fashion toward a common goal.[19] All decision-makers in such a networked structure must have a reasonably good, shared understanding of the operation in order to make decisions consistent with the overall intent.

PIGEAU AND MCCANN'S CONCEPTUAL FRAMEWORK OF COMMON INTENT

The traditional military usage of command intent involves, to some extent, the sharing of a model of an operation rather than just a set of directives or tasks. Directives on their own do not allow the sort of initiative and synchronization demanded in modern operations. Thus, Pigeau and McCann have advanced their fairly radical re-conceptualization of command and control in terms of shared intent.[20]

Pigeau and McCann define intent as the general connotation of a specific purpose, not only the explicit statement of objectives. General intent is divided into two parts, explicit and implicit. Explicit intent consists of publicly communicated directions such as written or verbal orders. According to these scholars, explicit intent is only the tip of the iceberg in terms of communicating the full extent of intent. Even with lengthy directives, some intentions and details are left to unspoken expectations, are assumed, or are referred to only generally.

In contrast to the explicit, implicit intent is comprised of the internalized collective and individual knowledge, expectations and beliefs that guide a person's actions. Implicit intent is essential to understanding. Interpretation of an explicit communication will always be based on a rich network of implied meanings that qualify and elaborate upon the particular words. Thus, the concept of implicit intent refers to all of the connotations latent in an explicit communication.

With intent defined in terms of the explicit and implicit components, *common* intent is the sum of all communication, knowledge, ideas, beliefs, etc. that are shared among a set of people working on a common operation. Pigeau and McCann illustrate the relationship between the implicit and the explicit in the *intent hierarchy* or *pyramid* (see Figure 2-1), which indicates the relative importance and influence that they attach to the different components of intent by the area of the pyramid devoted to those components.[21] The top layer of explicit intent comprises knowledge that is derived from communications such as orders or directives, as well as dialogue about the mission in the form of discussion, questions and answers. Pigeau and McCann argue that this is the most visible but least influential aspect of intent because the explicit layer builds on all of the layers of implicit expectations that are based on personal, military and cultural education, training, and experience.

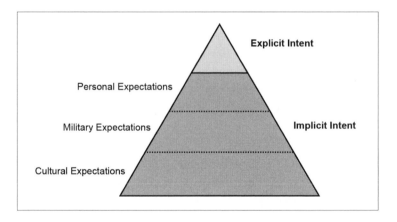

Figure 2-1: Intent Pyramid (Adapted from Pigeau & McCann, *The Human in Command.*)

Implicit intent is comprised of ever-increasing fundamental layers of expectations. The personal layer comprises the knowledge, beliefs and mental models derived through personal experience. The military layer is based in turn on a broader, more influential layer of general military expectations, comprised of doctrines and traditions that govern how operations should be carried out in general. Finally, the cultural layer is based on the broadest cultural expectations about national interests, societal norms and moral and ethical values.

In Pigeau and McCann's framework, the quality of command and control is a direct function of the extent to which all people in the organization share intent (both explicit and implicit). Many factors potentially determine the degree of common intent, including the organizational structure, the kinds of training available, and more broadly, the nature of the societal and cultural norms that have shaped how the people think and interact with one another. Individual qualities such as leadership can also greatly affect the sharing of intent and whether implicit intent is valued and fostered.

Ultimately, shared implicit intent is the most important aspect of command and the key determinant of success in an operation. To be sure, the greater the sharing of implicit intent, the more likely the group will work together both effectively and efficiently, and the less likely its members will misunderstand one another. Consequently, a potential problem of contemporary integrated operations will be the different implicit intents brought by individuals from different organizational cultures.

Explicit and implicit intent are assumed to be shared between people in different ways. Explicit intent is shared through explicit communication in some form (usually written or verbal directives) in venues such as planning meetings, rehearsals, or any other mission-related activity. In contrast, sharing implicit intent involves a more complicated and time-consuming set of activities that must be supported by the whole military organization. Education and training do more than convey explicit intent, they also convey implicit knowledge, expectations and values that people internalize. Social interaction is also the key to gaining shared implicit intent. Processes of socialization (observing and inferring from others' behaviour), externalization (of one's beliefs and attitudes), and internalization (of others' beliefs and attitudes) allow people to acquire implicit intent without explicit or conscious effort.

Although Pigeau and McCann's framework has had significant impact on military thinking, several key aspects require empirical validation. For example, although intent is depicted as a pyramid, there is no *a priori* evidence that the relative degrees of influence of the three implicit layers are distributed in such an orderly fashion. In fact, the three layers are closely interrelated, with military organizations created within a set of cultural expectations. Likewise, people are greatly influenced by the culture in which they are born and live. A culture, however, changes over time as a result of the influences of all the individuals and institutions that comprise it. Thus, it can be difficult to relate any aspect of an individual's or group's beliefs, attitudes or values exclusively to one particular layer of expectations.

THE CORE CONCEPTS OF INTENT

Further development of Pigeau and McCann's conceptual framework of common intent has helped to clarify how intent is formed and communicated.[22] We can also see how the framework brings together several important themes that have been evident in cognitive and military research for some time: 1) shared understanding is essential for coordinated and correct action; 2) a common framework for solving problems allows subordinate decision-makers to make decisions consistent with what the commander wants to achieve; and 3) shared knowledge and experience is the basis for good communication. The importance of these themes is evidenced by the fact that they have been independently explored by a number of researchers.

Shared Understanding. The first theme has been explored largely in the context of the concept of the mental model, which describes a complex and rich mental representation of knowledge.[23] A mental model is an organized knowledge representation in which internal, mental symbols correspond to elements making up an external system so that the model symbols are inter-related in the same fashion as the external elements. Although less detailed than reality, and emphasizing certain elements and relationships over others, a mental model nevertheless serves as an internal simulation of an external system.

The difficult part of command is *sharing* a mental model. The extent to which individuals share the same mental model for a common area of interest can be expected to affect the degree of coordination or simply behaviour in common – intentionally or otherwise. A number of empirical studies support this view. For teams to be effective in solving C2 problems, they must share the same perceptions of goals and contingencies.[24] Moreover, to work effectively toward a clear set of goals, team members should adopt the same mental model of the decision-making environment, including tasks, problems, assumptions, categories and issues.[25]

Sharing a mental model is very much like Pigeau and McCann's idea of establishing common intent. In both cases, groups of individuals function more effectively as a team if they share an organized and common knowledge structure that represents the functioning of the system, the task and the team itself. A shared mental model directs team members as to what roles they are to play, what tasks they are to perform, how to coordinate within the team by predicting each others' information needs and the likely behaviour of the system as a whole. Likewise, common intent conveys more than just team goals; it provides, among other things, the same kind of direction as a team mental model. The main difference between the two concepts seems to be in the level of focus or specificity of the shared representation. As examined in empirical studies, team mental models tend to focus on relatively narrow problem or task domains, defined in procedural terms rather than mission goals.

The use of implicit communication illustrates another benefit of shared mental models: they help team members to predict the needs and actions of other members, which allows them in turn to more effectively support other team members. For example, fast tempo C2 requires coordination of team members with different roles.[26] When individual team members fail to act appropriately and within time constraints, the team as a whole can fail. Thus, teams that are trained to instil mental models that better describe what a system is for, what it looks like, how it works, what it is currently doing and how it will likely behave can be expected to perform better, particularly in terms of communication and coordination.

Common Problem-Solving Framework. The concept of common intent is as much about creating a problem-solving environment as about recording the commander's objectives or plans. Pigeau and McCann frame intent in terms of the ability for decision-makers to reason to the same conclusions when confronted with unexpected events. In a similar vein, others have argued that the traditional statement of commander's intent is inadequate and should be developed into a broader command concept.[27] Their starting point was to consider the question of what a commander would have to tell his or her subordinates before an operation so that their subsequent actions would be consistent with his or her intent. Identifying numerous specific aspects of a good command concept, researchers have emphasized an awareness of potential problems and opportunities, indicators of problems in the plan, and perhaps most important, an understanding of the kinds of information the commander will need to evaluate the progress of the operation.[28] This latter point is crucial in modern operations where the amount of data can quickly overwhelm any human decision-maker.

The command concept is the sum of knowledge required by subordinate commanders on which they will base their own planning and execution and that will act as a filter for the exchange of essential command related information before and during the operation. The ideal communication system will limit traffic to only that which answers essential questions with respect to the command concept, such as: "Are things going as envisioned? If not, what needs fixing? Why are things going wrong? Is the vision wrong or does it simply need some adjustment?"[29] Articulating the key command concepts for an operation bounds the information needs of the commander and enables subordinate commanders to pass along only that information concerned with the command concept.

Some validation of this concept of command comes in the form of historical reviews of six modern battles. Although such historical analysis is subjective, key concepts were identified that had contributed to success (or failure when they were absent).[30] Based on historical analysis, an ideal command concept is a "hypothetical statement of the commander's intent that should have been, *under the doctrine, training, and common knowledge of the time*, clearly sufficient for subordinate commanders to successfully execute the responsibilities they were actually called on to fulfill during battle, without exchanging additional information with their superior commander" (emphasis added).

Tacit Knowledge (TK) is another concept that has been applied to military decision-making as a way to describe the kinds of shared skills and practical "know-how" expressed through action rather than articulated in words.[31] Thus, TK is similar to implicit intent – procedural, goal-related and acquired with little organizational support. Another similar concept is that of embedded knowledge.[32] Embedded knowledge is latent knowledge shared among team members as a potential resource for supporting teamwork and collaboration. Synergistic interaction among individuals can produce a group product superior to the sum of individual contributions, that is, the organization will act as though it has greater knowledge than all of its members.

Common Basis for Communication. Perhaps the most fundamental role for common intent is in communication. Language is a tool with which we attempt to create in others' minds an understanding. In particular, rather than attempt to exhaustively and definitively state all of the information we wish to convey, people are skilled at stating things that call upon connotations to elicit implicit knowledge that would be difficult or impossible to convey explicitly. The concept of *common ground* has been developed to address this issue.[33] It is argued that people do not have to explicitly express the majority of information underlying a message. Instead, they rely on the vast knowledge of the addressee to allow comprehension.

Like common intent, common ground consists of the mutual knowledge, beliefs and assumptions held by people.[34] This mutual knowledge defines concepts and ideas that can be referred to with simple messages, which elicit extensive and detailed memories from the recipient. These remembered concepts become part of the communication. Thus, if one knows that certain experiences or concepts are shared, one can attempt to bring about a state of understanding in another by probing with key words or expressions that will likely elicit the intended ideas.

Communication has been described as a process of coordination in which participants present explicit messages to others who interpret them with respect to their vast stores of experiences and knowledge. Feedback is given to indicate acceptance and understanding of the message or a lack of understanding and requests to clarify or elaborate.[35] The whole process is collaborative as participants try to reach a mutual belief that each party has understood the previous messages.[36]

Numerous experimental studies have validated the concept and explore the role of common ground in communication. Not much of this research, however, has been conducted in large-scale, naturalistic settings, which makes it difficult to ascertain exactly how the concept of common ground operates in an organizational context. We do not know, for example, how common ground develops in, and is influenced by, the structure and practices of an organization such as the Canadian Forces.

Although people require a great deal of shared knowledge in order to communicate efficiently and effectively, they have been found to naturally employ a range of communication techniques that tailor messages to their addressees.[37] These processes can be extended to communication in military organizations and support the basic premises of Pigeau and McCann's framework of common intent, specifically the shared concepts, terminology and communication protocols that people develop to communicate effectively. Military organizations are famous (or perhaps infamous) for developing their own jargon, which is often impenetrable to outsiders. The research on common ground, however, indicates that this actually goes well beyond just specialized terms and names. A military organization likely develops multiple specialized "proto-languages" containing their own words, concepts, grammatical structures and protocols for ensuring mutual understanding.

COMMON INTENT: A VALID CONSTRUCT?

Pigeau and McCann's concept of common intent provides a rich framework in which to think about C2. It highlights the extent to which human understanding, and sharing of understanding, is involved in planning and carrying-out an operation. To transform the concept of common intent into a practical, testable theory that can guide research and development of doctrine, training and so on, scholars need to be able to measure intent as well as C2 performance. The key requirement of a theory is to provide a link between prediction and observation, and that depends on the theory providing an accurate model of reality.

Construct validation implies the expression of a set of theoretical concepts and their interrelations (i.e., the conceptual net), the development of ways to measure those constructs proposed by the theory, and the empirical testing of the hypothetical relations among the constructs and their associated observable manifestations.[38] The validation process is ongoing and requires multiple iterations over time, some of which may entail a refinement of the construct and its measures.[39]

Experts in the field of psychometric theory, such as Jum Nunnally and Ira Bernstein, have identified two major scientific concerns: 1) developing measures of individual constructs, and, 2) finding functional relations between those measures. Thus, any theory has two equally significant components, a measurement component and a structural component.[40] The logic behind constructs defining individual differences is exactly the same as that behind those defining experimental manipulations. The structural component suggests that measures should be evaluated within broader theoretical models that include the causes, correlates and effects of the construct of interest and how they relate to one another. This would then provide evidence that measures of a construct exhibit relationships with measures of other constructs in accordance with relevant theory.

Although common intent is similar in many respects to command concepts, shared mental models and common ground, it is not clear whether we can adapt measurement strategies from these areas or whether we must develop an entirely new paradigm. Of course, prior to beginning a lengthy and costly measurement process, we need to assess whether the construct of common intent *can* be measured, as some constructs are so abstract they may not be amenable to measurement.[41] Similarly, the need for a measuring instrument, or set of instruments, also has to be assessed. Adequate instruments may already exist that capture part, or all, of the construct of common intent; the value of a new measure should be large relative to the costs of its development. To be useful, a new instrument should also demonstrate some theoretical or empirical advantage over existing measures of the same construct, being either more accurate or more efficient (e.g., shorter, cheaper, more user-friendly).[42]

By conceptualizing the theory of common intent in terms of mental structures or representations of knowledge, beliefs and values that guide team interaction, we are able to propose a conceptual "net" implied by this theory.[43] Assuming internal consistency, construct validity would be evident should the purported measure(s) of the construct behave as expected. In other words, the measures must fit into the net of expected relationships established for the construct of common intent.[44] This implies that we need to conduct studies and/or experiments to determine the extent to which the measures of common intent are consistent with the hypotheses about the construct.

The question of whether common intent is a valid construct goes beyond just the issue of measurement. It must also address whether we can manipulate aspects of intent to produce predicted results. Thus, in operationalizing elements of intent, we create the means to affect intent as well as to measure it. Indeed, the process of construct validation is like that of theory development because theory and validity are integrally linked. The theoretical relevance of a construct depends on its validity, a judgment of the degree to which a measure truly reflects the construct it is purportedly measuring.[45] Likewise, without a sound theory, there can be no construct validity.

The process of construct validation is possible only to the extent that some of the statements in the theoretical model lead to predicted relations among observables, that is, the model must be explicit enough so that validating evidence may be properly interpreted.[46] Many types of evidence are relevant to construct validity, such as predictions of group differences, changes with time or after-experimental manipulation, and correlations. High correlations and stability may constitute favourable or unfavourable evidence for the proposed interpretation, depending on the model in which the construct is situated.

The prediction of correlations often involves the use of a multi-trait-multi-method matrix (MTMM) or a factor analytic procedure. MTMM data define two or more constructs measured by two or more methods, leading to a matrix that resembles a standard correlation matrix. Correlations between measures of related constructs should be high, suggesting convergent validity, whereas correlations between measures of unrelated constructs should be low, supporting discriminant validity.[47]

Approaches to construct validation have been further separated into classical, modern and emerging approaches.[48] As such, the evaluation of construct validity should no longer rely on MTMM data and researchers should model these relationships via second-order (confirmatory) factor analysis. Factor analytic models are appropriate most of the time, yet more complex models should probably be favoured in some cases (e.g., second-order factor models).

When a prediction fails to occur, the reason may lie in the proposed interpretation of the measure or in the network.[49] If the data do not support the predictions: 1) the experiment may have been flawed; 2) the theory may be wrong and should be revised; or 3) the measure may not capture the construct.[50] The researcher can alter the network by redefining the construct under study, but must validate any new interpretation of the measure by collecting a fresh body of data.[51] Construct validation is an ongoing process and it cannot be inferred from a single set of observations or expressed in the form of a single validity coefficient. Neither can the integration of diverse data into a proper judgment be an entirely quantitative process.[52]

THE QUESTION OF MEASUREMENT

Taking stock of the concept of common intent, it is apparent that no established paradigm for studying it has yet emerged.[53] There remains a keen need to identify the potential measures of intent as a first step to establishing the validity of the construct. Many questions pertaining to the construct of common intent remain pertinent, such as, has the construct been defined clearly enough so that researchers in the area can agree on its content domain? Is the construct of common intent even amenable to operationalization and measurement? If so, can existing strategies used for the measurement of constructs in the conceptual net be adapted for the purposes of operationalizing and measuring common intent? Were these measures carefully and competently developed? What is its surrounding conceptual net (i.e., precursors, correlates and effects)? What type of validity evidence is most relevant in this context?

As a matter of fact, it will likely be necessary to rely upon the validation strategies discussed in this chapter (i.e., predictions of group differences, changes after experimental manipulation, correlations, etc.), using a mix of approaches including confirmatory factor analysis.

It is indisputable that the theoretical boundaries of the construct of common intent, as well as its dimensionality, need to be further explored. Can common intent be structured in the same way as a shared mental model, that is, with task, team and contextual components? Or should we conceptualize implicit intent as a higher-order construct, with knowledge, attitudes, beliefs and values forming the lower-order constructs that need to be operationalized in different contexts? In addressing these questions, we confront the potential uses and benefits, as well as the potential limitations, of measurement approaches that already exist.

Quality of Command Intent. The focus of C2 research is often on the processes of acquiring, sorting and acting upon information, but the true focus of command itself is on the successful accomplishment of goals. Thus, a key consideration when considering intent is the quality of the command intent in terms of plans and decisions.[54] Effective C2 is predicated upon the completeness and appropriateness of command concepts as well as upon processes for sharing intent. But assessing the quality of command intent is a challenge, as outcome-based measures (e.g., mission success) have been shown to be less appropriate for assessing command issues. Not only are they difficult to judge objectively, they are also dependent on other factors such as enemy reaction, correctness of intelligence estimates or relative capabilities.

The alternative to outcome-based measures is to assess the quality of command intent on the basis of process-related criteria such as whether the command intent is deemed appropriate for mission success. Here too, measurement pitfalls await. The appropriateness of a plan is difficult to quantify because military plans are complex, mission-specific and there are few universally agreed upon criteria for defining success. Consequently, opinions as to quality are likely to vary widely and consensus judgments will be difficult to achieve.

Appropriate measures of quality of intent might include consensus of expert opinion, completeness of coverage, probability of misinterpretation and adaptability to unforeseen circumstances. In addition to these subjective measures, more objective but indirect measures can be developed based on indicators of misunderstanding. This would require one to identify behavioural indicators that are reliably associated with difficulty understanding or implementing command intent.

The primary procedures for assessing the quality of intent will likely be ratings made by experts in military operations and planning. Whether ratings are performed in real-time or through post-event review and analysis of data logs, careful consideration must be paid to the role that the experts' experience, training and biases will play in their judgment. Having pre-defined attributes or specific criteria pertaining to the objectives to be achieved is essential for greater precision of ratings.

Shared Mental Models. The concept of a shared mental model captures several key elements of common intent, most noticeably the rich and shareable knowledge structures that people acquire and use in a wide range of team activities, such as communication and coordination.[55] Thus, measures of shared mental models can be adapted to assess the knowledge, attitudes and behaviours implicit in shared intent.

Shared mental models can be measured from several different perspectives: 1) the *content* of the mental model, or measures to identify what people know; 2) the *organization* of knowledge, or measures to uncover and depict conceptual relationships among items of knowledge; and 3) the *sharing* of the same mental model between people, or measures to assess the overlap in content and organization between the mental models of individuals.[56] Although all of these forms of measure are necessary to fully explore the role of shared mental models in teams, the aspects of content and structure are most important. The issue of content concerns its relation to formal command intent and the extent to which it supports a common understanding of objectives and methods.[57] The structure of the mental model, in contrast, most directly relates to how a team will work together. The common subdivision of team mental models into *team, task* and *resources* components is a way to understand how the structure of the model affects team processes.[58]

The primary methods of assessing the content of mental models are knowledge surveys and interview techniques, both of which probe for knowledge items. The structure of mental models can be assessed through conceptual mapping techniques, such as card sorting with multidimensional scaling or cluster analysis.[59] Assessing the overlap of mental models among individuals requires knowledge surveys and conceptual mapping, as well as statistical analysis techniques to compute the degree of similarity among knowledge and the organization of representations.

Coordination. Coordination is central to effective teamwork. Coordination, however, can be difficult to operationalize, especially when distinguishing it from communication and individual contributions to team functioning. The precursors of team coordination are largely covered by measures of team mental models (i.e., the correctness of expectations about team members, tasks and roles). Beyond this, however, measures of coordination must also address the coordination of tasks and information, and the group processes and motivational issues underlying effective coordination.

Coordination has to be measured in the complete context of preparation and conduct of a team-based mission. Issues concerning assessment of coordination include the processes or strategies team members are using to work together as a unit, how the team's coordination contributes to successful performance, the factors that affect the coordination strategies adopted, and the learning process underlying the members' coordination strategies.

Assessing the effectiveness of coordination requires measures of team performance, which can be task-based indicators of success (i.e., outcomes related to the completion of specific tasks or achievement of goals) or general indicators of success, such as expert ratings of effectiveness.[60] For the most part, measures will seek to relate the presence or absence and degree of intensity of a particular team process (e.g., openness to ideas or levels of affective conflict) or feature (e.g., diversity, trust in other members' commitment) to some aspect of team efficiency or effectiveness. Measurement of team process can lead to a problem of circularity, with trust, commitment, motivation and shared responsibility being determining factors for individuals to implement group processes and, in turn, these group processes leading to trust and commitment which, in turn, lead to more effective coordination.

Constructs related to cooperation will often be operationalized through surveys or questionnaires, although observers can also identify and rate pertinent behavioural indicators. Expert ratings can be used to assess coordination processes as long as the dimensions for rating, such as appropriateness of communication and degree of helping, have been defined and validated. Another, more objective approach is to assess behavioural indicators of team coordination, such as helping other members, transferring appropriate information and so on. Assessing these indicators, however, requires continuous observation of a team at work, which can be difficult if the teams are observed in real-time. Recording the team's activities by video and/or audio log allows for more thorough analysis but may be impractical in some situations. Some measures can be obtained through the embedded or freeze probe methods, in which team members periodically provide self ratings or answers to questions that indicate relative coordination.

Communication. Communication, whether verbal or written, is the process by which explicit intent is shared, but it is also a key component of many processes involved in sharing implicit intent.[61] The relation between communication and intent also flows in the other direction, as communication depends on the values, attitudes and procedures shared among people.

The effectiveness of communication is generally measured in terms of the degree of understanding achieved by individuals, which is often assessed by comparing responses to questionnaires by the individuals. The efficiency of communication can be measured in terms of the shared effort required to achieve a level of understanding, by indicators such as transmission time and the number of requests for clarification. Thus, one measurement approach is to assess the receiving party's understanding against the intended understanding of the transmitting party. This technique entails the same kinds of measures of knowledge content and structure as used to assess mental models.

Given the richness of human communication, real-time assessment is very difficult. The main method for measuring communication variables is the analysis of a video or audio log of communication among team members so that observers have sufficient time to identify critical aspects, such as the volume (i.e., amount) of communication, types of utterances (e.g., questions, information transfers, etc.), direction, anticipation and so on. Other measures may include levels of confidence on the part of sender, receiver or listener that the communication has been comprehended with this level of confidence being related to different components of the mental models of the communicators.

Cultural diversity presents an interesting potential challenge to researchers in real-world settings. Technical advances, such as the enabling of distributed teams, increase the likelihood that teams will be composed of members from different organizational or national cultures. Multicultural entities will likely experience stresses with respect to cohesion, communication and coordination.[62] In addition, the cognitive frame members apply to problems and interactions will differ in many ways, affecting how individuals respond to measuring instruments. Conducting cross-cultural organizational research in such contexts comes with its own set of challenges that includes ascertaining whether the measuring instrument is appropriate for all cultures under study, whether the measure is reliable and valid within and across cultures, and whether the instrument is ethically acceptable.[63]

PROSPECTS FOR THEORETICAL DEVELOPMENT

Researchers in charge of developing and implementing measurement within operational settings face a variety of challenges due to the complexity of those environments.[64] Insofar as common intent is a construct specifically developed for an applied setting, we can expect its validation to be no small undertaking. The obstacles range from the practical (e.g., limited resources and broad scope of concepts to be measured) to the conceptual (e.g., developing agreed-upon definitions and linking measures to concepts). Yet, the full potential of common intent, as concerns its benefit to the military, will not be achieved without its development as a valid theory.

Despite difficulties, it will be possible to validate the construct of common intent. To alleviate some of the practical issues, subject matter experts (SMEs) from the operational environment can be involved in the measurement process. Researchers and SMEs working together can maximize the practicality, diagnosticity, validity (including face validity) and reliability of the measures. The investment in creating measures should be considered an organizational investment with the potential for great benefits to the organizations under scrutiny as well as the researchers.[65] Obtaining such "buy-in" from military organizations requires a practical theory-based measurement approach with a clear purpose that drives the process of creating measures.[66]

ENDNOTES

1   David Alberts and Richard Hayes, *Planning: Complex Endeavors* (Washington, D.C.: CCRP Publication Series, 2007).

2   Arthur Cebrowski and John Garstka, "Network Centric Warfare: Its Origin and Future," *US Naval Institute Proceedings* 124 (1998), 28-35; David Alberts and Richard Hayes, *Power to the Edge: Command ... Control ... in the Information Age* (Washington, D.C.: CCRP Publication Series, 2003); and, David Alberts, J.J. Garstka and F.P. Stein, *Network Centric Warfare: Developing and Leveraging Information Age Superiority* (Washington, D.C.: CCRP Publication Series, 1999).

3   Allan English, Richard Gimblett and Howard Coombs, *Networked Operations and Transformation: Context and Canadian Contributions* (Montreal and Kingston: McGill-Queen's University Press, 2007); P. Essens, M. Spaans and W. Treurniet, "Agile Networking in Command and Control," *The International C2 Journal* 1 (2007), 177-210; Michael Thomson and Barbara Adams, "Network Enabled Operations: A Canadian Perspective," Contractor Report CR-2005-162 (DRDC – Toronto, 2005); and, L. Warne, Irena Ali, Derek Bopping, Dennis Hart and Celina Pascoe, "The Network Centric Warrior: The Human Dimension of Network Centric Warfare," Client Report DSTO-CR-0373 (Defence Science and Technology Organization, 2004).

4   Peter Gizewski and Michael Rostek, "Toward a JIMP-Capable Land Force," *Canadian Army Journal* 10 (2007), 55-72.

5   Canada, Privy Council Office, *Securing an Open Society: Canada's National Security Policy* (2004). Available online at www.pco-bcp.gc.ca. See also, Canada, Department of National Defence [DND], *A Role of Pride and Influence in the World: Canada's International Policy Statement* (2005). Available online at www.forces.gc.ca.

6   English et al., *Networked Operations and Transformation*, Chapter 4.

7   For a recent review, see Edward Smith, *Complexity, Networking and Effects Based Approaches to Operations* (Washington, D.C.: CCRP Publication Series, 2007).

8   For a recent discussion see Alberts and Hayes, *Planning*.

9   Stacey Connaughton and Marissa Shuffler, "Multinational and Multicultural Distributed Teams," *Small Group Research* 38 (2007), 387-412; Michelle Marks,

Leslie DeChurch, John Mathieu, Frederick Panzer and Alexander Alonso, "Teamwork in Multi-team Systems," *Journal of Applied Psychology* 90 (2005), 964-971.

10   Ross Pigeau and Carol McCann, "Redefining Command and Control," in C. McCann and R. Pigeau, eds., *The Human in Command* (New York: Plenum Press, 2000), 163-184. For further discussion, see Keith Stewart, "Mission Command: Elasticity, Equilibrium, Culture and Intent," Technical Report TR-2006-254 (DRDC – Toronto, 2006), and, Keith Stewart, "The Structure and Measurement of Intent: A Review," Technical Report TR-2006-278 (DRDC – Toronto, 2006).

11   Robert Guion, *Assessment, Measurement and Prediction for Personnel Decisions* (Hillsdale, NJ: Erlbaum, 1998).

12   Lee Cronbach and Paul Meele, "Construct Validity in Psychological Tests," *Psychological Bulletin* 52 (1955), 281-302.

13   Jum Nunnally and Ira Bernstein, *Psychometric Theory*, 3rd ed. (New York: McGraw-Hill, 1994).

14   Richard Netemeyer, William Bearden and Subhash Sharma, *Scaling Procedures: Issues and Applications* (London: Sage Publications, 2003).

15   Nunnally and Bernstein, *Psychometric Theory*.

16   Lawrence Shattuck, "Communication of Intent in Distributed Supervisory Control Systems," (Unpublished Dissertation, Ohio State University, 1996).

17   Canada, DND, *The Infantry Section and Platoon in Battle*, Land Force, Vol. 1, The Conduct of Land Ops, B-GL-309-003/FT-001 (2000).

18   David Bryant, "Rethinking OODA: Toward a Modern Cognitive Framework of Command Decision Making," *Military Psychology* 18 (2006), 183-206.

19   Cebrowski and Garstka, "Network Centric Warfare."

20   Ross Pigeau and Carol McCann, "Putting 'Command' Back into Command and Control," Paper presented at the *Command and Control Conference*, Canadian Defence Preparedness Association, Ottawa, Ontario, 1995.

21   Pigeau and McCann, "Redefining Command and Control."

22   Ross Pigeau and Carol McCann, "Establishing Common Intent: The Key to Co-ordinated Military Action," in Allan D. English, ed., *The Operational Art: Canadian Perspectives – Leadership and Command* (Kingston: Canadian Defence Academy Press, 2006), 85-108.

23   P.N. Johnson-Laird, *Mental Models* (Cambridge, MA: Harvard University Press, 1983).

24   Tamer Basar and J.B. Cruz, Jr., "Robust Team-Optimal and Leader-Follower Policies for Decision Making in C3 Systems," Final Report ONR Contract No. N00014-82-K-0469 (Arlington, VA: Office of Naval Research, 1984); Carl Builder, Steven Bankes and Richard Nordin, *Command Concepts: A Theory Derived from the Practice of Command and Control* (Santa Monica, CA: RAND Corporation, 1999); and, T.S. Heffner, "Training Teams: The Impact of Task and Team Skills Training on the Relationship Between Mental Models and Team Performance," (Unpublished Dissertation, Pennsylvania State University, 1997).

25   Susan Mohammed, "Toward an Understanding of the Antecedents and Consequences of Shared Frames in a Group Decision-Making Context," (Unpublished Dissertation, Ohio State University, 1996).

26   W.B. Rouse, J.A. Cannon-Bowers and E. Salas, "The Role of Mental Models in Team Performance in Complex Systems," *IEEE Transactions on Systems, Man, & Cybernetics* 22 (1992), 1296-1308.

27   Builder et al., *Command Concepts.*

28   Ibid.

29   Ibid.

30   Ibid.

31   J.A. Horvath, G.B. Forsythe, P.J. Sweeney, J.A. McNally, J. Wattendorf, W.M. Williams and R.J. Sternberg, "Tacit Knowledge in Military Leadership: Evidence from Officer Interviews," Final Report ARI TR-1018 (Alexandria, VA: U.S. Army Research Institute for the Behavioral and Social Sciences, 1994); J.A. Horvath, W.M. Williams, G.B. Forsythe, P.J. Sweeney, R.J. Sternberg, J.A. McNally and J. Wattendorf, "Tacit Knowledge in Military Leadership: A Review of the Literature," Final Report ARI TR-1017 (Alexandria, VA: U.S. Army Research Institute for the Behavioral and Social Sciences, 1994); and, R.J. Sternberg and

R.K. Wagner, "Promoting Individual and Organizational Productivity Through Practical Intelligence: The Role of Tacit Knowledge in Personal and Organizational Effectiveness," Final Report ARI Research Note 91-52 (Alexandria, VA: U.S. Army Research Institute for the Behavioral and Social Sciences, 1991).

32   Ravindranath Madhavan and Rajiv Grover, "From Embedded Knowledge to Embodied Knowledge: New Product Development as Knowledge Management," *Journal of Marketing* 62, 4 (1998), 1-12.

33   Susan Brennan and Herbert Clark, "Conceptual Pacts and Lexical Choice in Conversation," *Journal of Experimental Psychology: Learning, Memory and Cognition* 22, 6 (1996), 1482-1493; Herbert Clark and Susan Brennan, "Grounding in Communication," in L.B. Resnick, J. Levine and S.D. Behrend, Eds., *Perspectives on Socially Shared Cognition* (Washington, D.C.: American Psychological Association, 1991), 127-149; Ellan Isaacs and Herbert Clark, "References in Conversation Between Experts and Novices," *Journal of Experimental Psychology: General* 116, 1 (1987), 26-37; and, Michael Schober and Herbert Clark, "Understanding by Addresses and Overhearers," *Cognitive Psychology* 21 (1989), 211-232.

34   Clark and Brennan, "Grounding in Communication."

35   Ibid.

36   Ibid.

37   Brennan and Clark, "Conceptual Pacts."

38   Lee Anna Clark and David Watson, "Constructing Validity: Basic Issues in Scale Development," *Psychological Assessment* 7 (1995), 309-319.

39   Netemeyer, Bearden and Sharma, *Scaling Procedures.*

40   Nunnally and Bernstein, *Psychometric Theory.*

41   Ibid.

42   Netemeyer, Bearden and Sharma, *Scaling Procedures.*

43   Cronbach and Meele, "Construct Validity."

44   Ibid.

45   Netemeyer, Bearden and Sharma, *Scaling Procedures.*

46   Cronbach and Meele, "Construct Validity."

47   Mary Allen and Wendy Yen, *Introduction to Measurement Theory* (Monterey: Brooks/Cole, 1979).

48   Jeffrey Edwards, "Construct Validation in Organizational Behavior Research," in J. Greenberg, ed., *Organizational Behavior: The State of the Science*, 2nd Ed. (Mahwah, NJ: Erlbaum, 2003), 327-371.

49   Cronbach and Meele, "Construct Validity."

50   Allen and Yen, *Introduction to Measurement Theory.*

51   Cronbach and Meele, "Construct Validity."

52   Ibid.

53   Keith Stewart, "The Structure and Measurement of Intent."

54   Builder et al., *Command Concepts.*

55   Kurt Kraiger and Lucy Wenzel, "Conceptual Development and Empirical Evaluation of Measures of Shared Mental Models as Indicators of Team Effectiveness," in M.T. Brannick and Eduardo Salas, eds., *Team Performance Assessment and Measurement: Theory, Methods and Applications* (Mahwah, NJ: Erlbaum, 1997), 63-84.

56   David Bryant, R.D.G. Webb, M.L. Matthews and P. Hausdorf, "Common Intent: A Review of the Literature," Contract Report CR 2001-041 (DRDC – Toronto, 2001).

57   Builder et al., *Command Concepts.*

58   Heffner, "Training Teams;" Mohammed, "Toward an Understanding;" and, Rouse et al., "The Role of Mental Models."

59   Pat Federico, "Expert and Novice Recognition of Similar Situations," *Human Factors* 37, 1 (1995), 105-122; J.B. Kruskal and M. Wish, *Multidimensional Scaling* (Beverly Hills, CA: Sage, 1978); and, Canada, DND, *Land Force Command*, Canadian Forces Publication 300(3), B-GL-300-003/FP-000 (1996).

60   Peter J.M.D. Essens, Ad.L.W. Vogelaar, Jacques J.C. Mylle, Carol Blend-ell, Carol Paris, Stanley M. Halpin and Joseph V. Baranski, "Team Effectiveness in Complex Settings: A Framework for Commanders," in Eduardo Salas, Gerald F. Goodwin and Shaun Burke, eds., *Team Effectiveness in Complex Organizations: Cross-Disciplinary Perspectives and Approaches* (Hillsdale, NJ: Lawrence Erlbaum and Associates, 2007).

61   Pigeau and McCann, "Redefining Command and Control."

62   E. Salas, C.S. Burke and J.E. Fowlkes, "Measuring Team Performance 'in the wild:' Challenges and Tips," in W. Bennett, C.E. Lance and D.J. Woehr, eds., *Performance Measurement: Current Perspectives and Future Challenges* (New York: Psychology Press, 2006), 245-272.

63   M.J. Gelfand, J.L. Raver and K. Holcombe Ehrhart, "Methodological Issues in Cross-Cultural Organizational Research," in S. Rogelberg, ed., *Handbook of Industrial and Organizational Psychology Research Methods* (New York: Blackwell, 2002), 216-241.

64   Salas et al., "Measuring Team Performance."

65   Ibid.

66   D.J. Dwyer and E. Salas, "Principles of Performance Measurement for Ensuring Aircrew Training Effectiveness," in H.F. O'Neil and D.H. Andrews, eds., *Aircrew Training and Assessment* (Mahwah, NJ: Erlbaum, 2000), 223-244.

CHAPTER 3

Judging Intention: Integrating Insights from Cognitive Science and Neuroscience

Oshin Vartanian

DEFENCE RESEARCH AND DEVELOPMENT CANADA – TORONTO

INTRODUCTION

While the philosophical literature on intentionality is vast, it has contributed little to our understanding of the *psychological* processes that underlie our ability to judge intention in others. Fortunately, this is beginning to change. Recent insights from cognitive science and neuroscience have shed new light on this issue by highlighting some of the psychological processes that mediate the judgment of intention in others. Most of the experimental evidence has, interestingly, been generated in studies of phenomena that are related to intention, rather than studies of intention *per se*, such as theory of mind, moral cognition, free will and psychopathology.

The aim of this chapter is to review some of the key findings from these areas, as well as the contributions made by these new strands of knowledge to the problem of judgment of intention. The focus will be strictly on how a mind judges intention in other *agents*, defined as individual minds or entities that can embody intent (e.g., governments). The ways in which judgments of intention at the individual level translate into shared judgments of intent at the group level constitute a different problem altogether and fall beyond the scope of this chapter, although that issue is dealt with in detail in other contributions made to this volume (e.g., Bryant, Blais and Baranski, and Stewart).

In addition, the problem of free will always lurks in the background when considering judgment of intention. Specifically, can an agent be held responsible for an act given that in the absence of free will the act could not have been an intentional one? Recent scientific evidence casts doubt on the very notion of free will – a necessity for most notions of malicious intent. This new scholarship suggests that it may be time to revisit some long-held beliefs about how humans are motivated toward action by self-generated intentions. The gist of this work is that free will is not an all-or-nothing phenomenon, but rather a matter of degree.[1] For example, free will may play a bigger role in planning actions than when actions are actually initiated.[2] Paradoxically, this implies that when deciding whether an agent exercised free will, we should focus on distal cognitions that informed the formation of the decision (e.g., planning an attack) rather than proximal causes that initiated the action (e.g., detonating a bomb). This has implications for command intent as well because it highlights the importance of conscious goal-setting in establishing intent relative to micromanaging action at the point of execution.

This chapter is organized as follows. First, I will introduce the concept of theory of mind and review recent literature that supports it. I will then discuss its implications in judging intention in others and how it can be used to potentially alter those intentions to one's advantage. Next, I will introduce findings from the literature investigating the link between theory of mind and moral cognition and how this can be applied to understanding factors that may influence the assessment of adversarial intent. This will be followed by an introduction of recent evidence from psychology as well as neuroscientific and neuropsychological studies of criminology and psychopathology that have a bearing on the link between intent and free will. Finally, I will close with a discussion of the role of theory of mind and free will in command intent.

THEORY OF MIND (TOM)

An area of inquiry that has great bearing on how we judge intention in others is theory of mind. TOM is the ability to make inferences about other people with respect to their independent mental states, such as their beliefs, desires, emotions and intentions.[3] For example, suppose that you are a passenger waiting to board a plane at an airport. A fellow passenger whom you do not know leaves her backpack under her seat and walks away. While she is away, an airport official, weary of the suspicious backpack that has been left unattended, collects it and takes it to the security desk. When the passenger returns, where will she look for the backpack? It goes without saying that she will look under her seat where she left it. Why? Because you know that your fellow passenger has the belief that the backpack is still located under her seat. The fact that you made reference to her belief to predict her behaviour indicates that you relied on TOM.

TOM is almost without question a uniquely human ability. It is an ability that is critical to human social interaction and we rely on it to predict and explain the behaviour of others in terms of their independent mental states. Furthermore, developmental data indicate that TOM does not develop until around the age of five, as children acquire the ability to mentally represent the minds of others. Interestingly, one typical task used to detect whether a child has developed TOM requires the child to engage in deception.[4] Deception would not be possible in the absence of TOM because in the course of deception we manipulate other people's beliefs, and by extension, their subsequent behaviour. The critical point here is that it would not be possible to manipulate other people's mental states to one's own advantage – be it their beliefs, desires, emotions or intentions – in the absence of TOM. Potential links between such strategic manipulation and defence-related and security-related issues will be made below in discussions of tactical deception and command intent.

COMPONENTS OF TOM

There is currently a consensus among researchers that TOM is not comprised of a unitary cognitive system; rather, it appears to be activated as a function of the interaction of a number of distinct cognitive abilities. There is brain-imaging data to support this componential organization of TOM. Here I will focus on three components. The first component is the ability to "decouple" mental states from reality. Returning to the airport example, it was critical to observe dissociation (decoupling) between the beliefs of your fellow passenger and the actual physical location of the backpack to judge the action of the passenger correctly. This decoupling enabled you to observe the difference between belief-driven perception and reality. Second, episodic and semantic memory would appear to be crucial for TOM.[5] This is not surprising given that one would draw on one's personal experience and knowledge regarding a specific situation to mentally simulate the mental states of another person in a similar situation. Third, TOM would seem to involve an analysis of the goals and outcomes of agents' actions, an ability that is linked closely with understanding causality and attributing intention. For example, to the extent that command intent involves causal linkages between goals and desired effects, TOM will be relevant in establishing these connections. As we will see below, specific aspects of this system may be more strongly involved in judgments of intention than judgments of other types of mental states.

TOM AND FALSE BELIEFS

An important feature of TOM is that it enables us to predict and explain behaviour in the face of conflict between an agent's mental state and reality. Take the airport example above: it was your fellow passenger's *false* belief that her backpack was underneath her seat that enabled you to predict her behaviour and not the reality of where her backpack actually was (i.e., at the security desk). In cases of false belief where there is a lack of correspondence between the belief of an agent and the reality of the situation, beliefs take precedence over reality in predicting and explaining behaviour. We know this to be the case because we possess TOM.

There is an additional catch. For you to be able to assess the effect of an agent's beliefs on his or her behaviour, you need to have some knowledge about the content of those beliefs. In the example offered above, in predicting the passenger's behaviour, you made an assumption about what the content of her belief was (i.e., "my backpack is underneath the seat"). Your assumption about the content of the passenger's belief was based on your general knowledge about the world, accumulated through experience. This suggests that to the extent that your knowledge about the world is faulty, you will generate faulty assumptions about the beliefs of others. It follows that the accuracy of our theories about what motivates the actions of others will have a direct bearing on our predictive ability regarding their mental states, including intentions.

This suggests that understanding the relationship between false beliefs and TOM is critical for judging intention in others. Unlike classical models of cognition in which thinking was viewed as a rule-governed and rational activity, there is increased appreciation in the cognitive sciences that thinking may resemble believing more than it does rule-governed reasoning.[6] Furthermore, there is also evidence across a wide array of experimental paradigms to suggest that human beings are prone to considering ideas they merely comprehend as true, unless those ideas are rejected as false following effortful deliberation regarding their validity.[7] Given that humans have limited information processing capacity, this suggests that any of us at any given point in time may believe in ideas that we have never scrutinized for validity. In other words, we are prone to maintaining *false* beliefs.

Given that our beliefs may be false, an interesting interplay may occur at the nexus of beliefs, intention and TOM. According to folk psychological theories of intention,[8] there is a difference in the way in which beliefs and desires on the one hand, and intentions on the other, are connected to actions. For example, in a causal chain of events, beliefs and desires are further away from actions than are intentions (see Figure 3-1).[9] This is because intentions emerge after the agent has reasoned consciously through potentially competing desires and formed a plan of action, which once decided upon, results in action. In other words, whereas beliefs and desires do not *imply* action, intentions do. According to folk psychological models of intention, having formed an intention implies that the agent has reasoned about the beliefs and desires to travel further down the causal route and has made a decision to act.

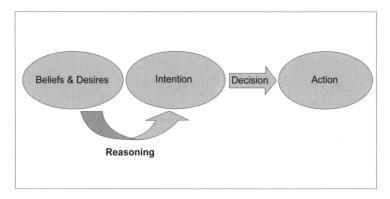

Figure 3-1: A Folk Psychological Model of Intention.

If recent cognitive science evidence is accurate, it is quite possible that people arrive at their intentions without having reasoned through their beliefs at all. If we treat false beliefs simply as representations about reality that do not correspond to reality, then this implies that the decoupling between belief and reality (a key component of the cognitive system that mediates TOM) is even more critical in judging intention. To judge the intention of another agent, it becomes necessary to take the perspective of the other agent, even if this necessitates assuming their false beliefs according to which their action makes sense. In the context of command intent, the extent to which a commander's intent is influenced by false beliefs would necessitate the acknowledgment of those false beliefs by subordinate commanders before an understanding of the commander's intent can be achieved. Although in some rudimentary sense our background knowledge about what we believe to be the true states of the world is important for judging intention, what is more important is perspective-taking that is mediated by a decoupling between beliefs and reality.

Within a defence and security context, this idea suggests that certain methods will be more fruitful for altering the intentions of adversarial parties than others. To alter the malicious intent of an adversary, according to methods derived from folk psychology (see Figure 3-1), one should employ methods that facilitate reasoning about those beliefs and desires. For example, supplying the adversary with information that may encourage a reassessment of his/her beliefs could potentially result in the retraction of malicious intent. However, given evidence suggesting that beliefs, false or otherwise, can cause intent in the absence of reasoning, a better method appears to be supplying the adversary with the opportunity to entertain competing beliefs. Switching to a different belief than the one that propagates the adversarial intention may be sufficient to sever that link.

For example, suppose that your forces have information indicating that the commander of an adversarial army has the false belief that you are planning to launch an attack against his/her country. Based on this false belief, this commander intends to engage in a pre-emptive strike, thus using the element of surprise to maximize military success. One could attempt to manipulate this commander's intent in at least two ways. The first would involve supplying the commander with accurate information (e.g., satellite imagery of border areas) that would cause a reassessment of the belief that you are planning to launch an attack against his/her country. Returning to our folk psychological model of intention (see Figure 3-1), this is analogous to saying that this information would be supplied with the aim to encourage reasoning leading to a rejection of the false belief. An alternative plan, however, could involve supplying the commander with information that facilitates the entertainment of other false beliefs, the aim being that those newly introduced beliefs would shift the causal chain away from the current intention (i.e., striking your forces) toward a new goal. Given that cognitive resources for information processing are particularly limited under conditions when multiple problems need to be addressed simultaneously, as would be expected during escalation of violence and conflict, this second alternative involving tactical deception may be more fruitful in manipulating intent than would the supply of accurate information.[10]

TOM AND MORAL COGNITION

As discussed above, TOM judgments involve making inferences about other people's states of mind. When we speculate about a person's intentions, we are by definition making a TOM judgment. In contrast, moral judgment involves making judgments about the moral acceptability of actions. For example, when we make a judgment about whether it is acceptable to kill in self-defence, we are making a moral judgment. Normally speaking, TOM judgments are made *prior* to making moral judgments. In other words, before we can assign blame to an agent (i.e., a moral judgment) for an action (e.g., killing), we must make some inferences about that agent's state of mind in relation to executing that action (i.e., a TOM judgment). Specifically, did the agent *intend* to kill? Thus, we arrive at a judgment about the agent's mental state first and then proceed to lay blame accordingly. Research in cognitive science has recently demonstrated that this process can work in reverse.[11] In a study from this literature, subjects were provided with the following vignette followed by the corresponding question:

> The vice-president of a company went to the chairman of the board and said, "We are thinking of starting a new program. It will help us increase profits, but it will also harm the environment." The chairman of the board answered, "I don't care at all about harming the environment. I just

want to make as much profit as I can. Let's start the new program." They started the new program. Sure enough, the environment was harmed.

Do you think the chairman *intentionally* harmed the environment?

Eighty-five per cent of the subjects said that the chairman intentionally harmed the environment. Note that no information about the chairman's intention was supplied in the vignette. In contrast, a strikingly different response pattern was found with the following vignette:[12]

The vice-president of a company went to the chairman of the board and said, "We are thinking of starting a new program. It will help us increase profits, and it will also help the environment." The chairman of the board answered, "I don't care at all about helping the environment. I just want to make as much profit as I can. Let's start the new program." They started the new program. Sure enough, the environment was helped.

Do you think the chairman *intentionally* helped the environment?

Here, only 23 per cent of subjects said the chairman intentionally helped the environment. Again, no information about the chairman's intention was supplied in the vignette. Note that the only difference between the two vignettes is that the by-product of the action involved either harming or helping the environment.

This particular pattern of results appears robust in that it has been replicated and extended in several subsequent studies.[13] Why does such a large difference exist in the assignment of intention to the chairman, considering that the only difference between the two vignettes is that the by-product of the action involved either harming or helping the environment? This effect has been explained by arguing that subjects' moral judgments regarding the action preceded their TOM judgments (See Figure 3-2).[14] In other words, subjects' perception of the action as blameworthy affected the assignment of intention, such that actions that were viewed as more blameworthy were also viewed as more intentional than actions that were viewed as less blameworthy. It appears that we believe intent plays a bigger role in decisions to harm than in decisions to help.[15]

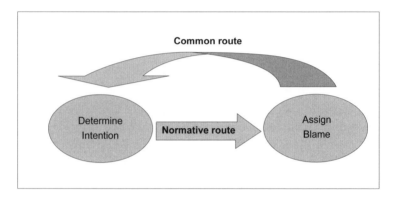

Figure 3-2: The Interplay between Moral Judgment and Theory of Mind (TOM).

This reversal effect (i.e., moral judgment preceding the judgment of intention) has important ramifications for the notion of determining adversarial intent within a defence and security setting.[16] Namely, the results suggest that we may assign various levels of intentionality to the action of an agent not based on information relevant to its intention, but rather as a function of the extent to which we view its action to result in harm or benefit to ourselves. Specifically, everything else being equal, we may be more likely to view as intentional those acts that are harmful rather than beneficial to the Canadian Forces (CF). For example, consider the following vignette:

> The government of country Y considered a strategy that would lead to a substantial increase in its own defensive

capability. The government of country Y was also aware that a by-product of implementing that strategy would involve harm to Canada's economic prosperity. The government of country Y decided that it was in its interest to boost its defensive capability and it thus implemented the strategy. Sure enough, the effect of the decision was to boost its defensive capability. In addition, the economic prosperity of Canada was harmed.

Do you think the government of country Y intentionally harmed Canada's economic prosperity?

If the results of earlier studies are any indication,[17] the majority of people would probably suggest that the government of country Y intentionally harmed Canada's economic prosperity. Now, consider the following vignette:

The government of country Y considered a strategy that would lead to a substantial increase in its own defensive capability. The government of country Y was also aware that a by-product of implementing that strategy would involve helping Canada's economic prosperity. The government of country Y decided that it was in its interest to boost its defensive capability and implemented the strategy. Sure enough, the effect of the decision was to boost its defensive capability. In addition, the economic prosperity of Canada was helped.

Do you think the government of country Y intentionally helped Canada's economic prosperity?

Again, if the results of earlier studies are any indication,[18] the majority of people would probably indicate that the government of country Y did not intentionally help Canada's economic prosperity. Note, that normatively speaking, the differential assignment of intention between the two cases constitutes an error in judgment because no information about country Y's intention was supplied in either vignette.

While the characterization of the action itself as blameworthy has ramifications for the assignment of intent, one can also contend that the choice of the specific actor used in the vignettes (i.e., chairman of the board) may have amplified the effect.[19] In other words, to the extent that our prior knowledge and beliefs bias us to think of a chairman of the board as more likely to act intentionally to harm rather than to help, we may be more inclined to assign intention to the chairman in the case of the former outcome than the latter. This suggests that quite apart from the nature of the act itself (i.e., helping vs. harming), our beliefs about the actor may also affect our judgments of intention. For example, consider the following vignette:

> Canada views country Y as an adversary. The government of country Y considered a strategy that would lead to a substantial increase in its own defensive capability. The government of country Y was also aware that a by-product of implementing that strategy would involve harm to Canada's economic prosperity. The government of country Y decided that it was in its interest to boost its defensive capability and implemented the strategy. Sure enough, the effect of the decision was to boost its defensive capability. In addition, the economic prosperity of Canada was harmed.
>
> Do you think the government of country Y intentionally harmed Canada's economic prosperity?

And compare it to the following vignette:

> Canada views country Y as an ally. The government of country Y considered a strategy that would lead to a substantial increase in its own defensive capability. The government of country Y was also aware that a by-product of implementing

that strategy would involve harm to Canada's economic prosperity. The government of country Y decided that it was in its interest to boost its defensive capability and implemented the strategy. Sure enough, the effect of the decision was to boost its defensive capability. In addition, the economic prosperity of Canada was harmed.

Do you think the government of country Y intentionally harmed Canada's economic prosperity?

Note, that while the outcome of country Y's action in both cases was harmful to Canada's economic prosperity, in the former case Canada considers country Y to be an adversary whereas in the latter case Canada considers country Y to be an ally. One could argue that those diverging considerations will have a strong impact on the judgment of the action as intentional, such that when country Y is viewed as an adversary, subjects may be more likely to consider the harm that results from its action as intentional compared to when country Y is viewed as an ally. This is another way of saying that a country's reputation (i.e., ally vs. adversary) and the degree of trust that such a reputation embodies will affect subjects' assignment of intention to its action. The same would be true in the context of command intent where one would expect the reputation of a commander to affect subordinates' assignment of intention to its action. Specifically, to the extent that subordinate commanders view the commander as trustworthy, the former would be less likely to view the latter's harmful actions as intentional.

In fact, there are experimental data from cognitive neuroscience that lend support to this prediction. For example, the brains of 48 pairs of volunteers were scanned with functional magnetic resonance imaging (fMRI) as they engaged in a two-person economic exchange game.[20] Unlike standard economic games (e.g., Ultimatum Game) where pairs of subjects typically complete a single exchange round,[21] subjects in this study completed ten consecutive exchange rounds. This design was employed to enhance the ecological validity of the study by allowing the development of reputation and trust between the partners across successive rounds. The researchers made the reasonable assumption that people develop internally represented models of their social partners through interaction and that these internal representations are in turn represented in brain substrates. Changes in the activation of the brain substrates should therefore predict behavioural changes in "intention to trust."

The game worked as follows: At the beginning of each trial, the "investor" was given 20 monetary units and instructed to split the 20 monetary units such that a certain amount was kept and the remainder entrusted to the "trustee." The trustee was then instructed to multiply the invested sum by three and to split that in any desired proportion between himself/herself and the investor. This decision ended the trial. Not surprisingly, the behavioural results demonstrated that reciprocity predicted trust. Two different types of reciprocity were identified. In the case of "benevolent" reciprocity, investors act generously (i.e., invest more) despite a decrease in repayment by the trustee. This builds trust in the trustee toward the investor. In contrast, in the case of "malevolent" reciprocity, the investor repays the trustee's generosity (i.e., more repayment) with investing less. This reduces trust in the trustee toward the investor. Neural results revealed that in trustees, there was significantly higher activation in a specific brain structure (i.e., head of the caudate) in trials involving benevolent than malevolent reciprocity. More important, as the game progressed, the peak of the activation in the head of the caudate shifted upstream in time, appearing *prior* to the revelation of the investor's actual decision. In other words, as the trustee built a better mental representation of the investor's mind as a generous partner, the trustee exhibited the "intention to trust" prior to the observation of overt behaviour by the investor. The key underlying idea presented here is that an agent's reputation as trustworthy affects our intention to trust them.[22]

Extending the findings concerning malevolent reciprocity to the defence and security domain suggests that to the extent that viewing an agent as "adversarial" denotes some indication of distrust in the motivations underlying his/her/its behaviour. This fact may affect our TOM judgments regarding the intentionality of his/her/its actions. In turn, this attribution of intention can have potentially detrimental consequences for understanding and predicting agents' behaviours, especially under conditions in which the situation is underdetermined. Specifically, the top-down influence of reputation and trust will make it more likely that the decision-maker will underweight disconfirmatory information and overweight confirmatory information. This may manifest itself especially strongly in situations where harm to self has occurred, exhibited by an overestimation of the intention of adversarial parties and an underestimation of the intention of allied parties to cause the harm, both of which constitute errors in judgment. This suggests a need to study the psychological underpinnings of the term "adversarial" and how consideration of intent is affected as a function of the connotations of the term "adversarial." This applies to issues of trust and reputation as much as it does to moral or otherwise negative judgments of blameworthiness.

INTENT AND FREE WILL

Judgments of intention are made against a backdrop of assumptions about free will. This is because assigning intent to the behaviour of an agent implies that we grant it free will. This is a foundational issue in western legal systems. To be sure, simply assuming that people can exercise free will is a different matter than whether there is any empirical evidence supporting this assumption. In fact, recent evidence from psychopathology, criminology and neuroscience suggests that there is little reason to believe that people have free will.[23] It goes without saying that if it were indeed the case that people could not be assumed to have free will, this would present great problems for the legality of actions taken against agents responsible for malicious acts against us.

There are two lines of evidence that should caution us against taking free will for granted. First, a number of laboratory electrophysiological studies have demonstrated that people become consciously aware of their intentions for performing actions around 200 milliseconds before an action is performed. However, this conscious awareness of the intention to act occurs *later* than the scalp recording of the so-called "readiness potential" prior to movement.[24] The readiness potential is a measure of electrophysiological activity in the motor cortex that leads up to voluntary muscle movement and therefore functions as a biological index of volition. This finding throws our folk psychological notions of agency into disarray by suggesting that individual actions may not follow conscious intentions. Rather, it seems that conscious intentions are formed following the initiation of action. Although this experimental paradigm has its share of critics,[25] the available evidence nevertheless poses a serious problem for the notion of free will. To the extent that free will necessitates holding an agent responsible for an act only if conscious intention was formed prior to exhibiting the act, experiments based on the readiness potential suggest that people become consciously aware of their acts only *after* they have been initiated.

Second, a large literature has been amassed that links disorders of the brain to disorders of behaviour, including criminal behaviour. Given that the prefrontal cortex is known to be involved in a diverse array of higher cognitive abilities such as empathy, regret, ethical decision-making, reasoning and inhibition of inappropriate behaviour, it is perhaps not surprising that pathologies of the prefrontal cortex have been linked with difficulties in the expression of those abilities.[26] More important, to the extent that those abilities are relevant to the formation of conscious intent in carrying out actions, this evidence implies difficulties in assuming free will in persons who engage in pathological criminal behaviour because their behaviours may be a manifestation of brain disorder rather than acts of free will *per se*.

If the link between disorders of the brain and disorders of behaviour including criminal behaviour is robust, then one would expect to find disproportionately high levels of medical disorders in criminal populations. This is indeed the case. The proportion of incarcerated criminals who are medically and legally incompetent to stand trial is 25 per cent.[27] In a systematic study of 62 surveys including 23,000 prisoners, the rates of psychosis and depressive illness were found to be several times higher than the rates found in the general, non-incarcerated population.[28] In fact, the rate of antisocial personality disorder, which itself has biological markers, was found to be ten times higher than the rate found in the general, non-incarcerated population. This evidence presents a serious problem for the notion of free will because to the extent that healthy brain tissue is a pre-requisite for the mental capacities necessary for making informed choices, the presence of disproportionately high levels of medical disorders within the criminal population may indicate that at least some criminals' brain pathology may be a significant contributor to the manifestation of their behaviour.

Quite aside from the specifics of the cases discussed above, the more important question raised by an examination of the laboratory and criminology evidence presented here is that scientifically speaking, the case for free will is currently rather weak. Nevertheless, as a foundational assumption it may be indispensable not only for law, but also for defence and security purposes. This is because from a legal perspective, it would be difficult to hold adversaries responsible for their actions unless free will was granted. This suggests that as parties interested in the role of intention in behaviour, we should follow developments that shed light on the psychological underpinnings of free will very closely, while remaining flexible about the extent to which free will can be taken for granted while assessing intent.

Some psychologists have suggested that free will may play a bigger role while making decisions rather than when actions are initiated.[29] This idea has implications for judgment of intention. Specifically, it implies that the critical factor for assigning intentionality to an action should not rest on whether the agent possessed free will at the time of executing the action, but rather whether the agent possessed free will when the action was planned or decided upon. In this light, the findings regarding the readiness potential are less damaging to the concept of free will. According to this literature, human beings are not characterized by a complete presence or absence of free will. Rather, they navigate along a continuum of control over behaviour.[30] The process of judging intention should therefore involve an assessment of the extent to which free will was exercised at the relevant juncture in the time course of an action from planning to execution.

LINKS WITH COMMAND INTENT

The discussion in this chapter has centred on how a mind judges intention in other agents. This is because the focus has been on the relation between the self and a malicious (adversarial) agent. Nevertheless, the role of TOM in judgment of intention extends to non-adversarial agents, and is relevant to the notion of command intent. As discussed elsewhere in this volume (e.g., Bryant, Blais and Baranski, and Stewart), command intent can be understood at the individual (i.e., commander's intent and the intents of individual subordinate commanders) and collective (i.e., common intent) levels, and can take implicit and explicit forms. The extent to which subordinate commanders are able to judge the intention of the commander successfully is also a function of TOM. Specifically, subordinate commanders must make accurate inferences about the mental states (e.g., beliefs) of the commander, especially under conditions where decoupling is required between the commander's mental state and external reality. Furthermore, the discussion on free will highlights the importance of conscious goal setting in the early establishment of intent (i.e., implicit and explicit) relative to micromanaging action at the point of execution. The literature suggests that the wilful planning of actions far ahead of their execution may play a more important role in establishing the intention to act than wilful control over the initiation of the action.

CONCLUSION

The aim of this chapter was to highlight the contribution that advances in cognitive science and neuroscience can make to the process of judging intention. The evidence suggests that our judgments of intention are influenced by factors that introduce error into the judgment process. Studies that highlight these factors and offer cognitive countermeasures are needed. In addition, the notion of free will, a necessity for commonsensical understandings of intended action, is questioned. It appears that human beings navigate along a continuum of free will. More importantly, free will may play a bigger role in the course of forming plans and making decisions than at the point when actions are actually initiated. From the perspective of Command Intent, this highlights the importance of goal definition in the early establishment of intent (i.e., implicit and explicit) relative to management of action at the point of execution.

ENDNOTES

1   Roy F. Baumeister, "Free Will in Scientific Psychology," *Current Directions in Psychological Science* 3 (2008), 14-19.

2   Peter M. Gollwitzer, "Implementation Intentions: Strong Effects of Simple Plans," *American Psychologist* 54 (1999), 493-503.

3   Christopher Frith and Uta Frith, "Theory of Mind," *Current Biology* 15 (2005), R644-R645.

4   Beate Sodian and Uta Frith, "Deception and Sabotage in Autistic, Retarded and Normal Children," *Journal of Child Psychology and Psychiatry and Allied Disciplines* 33 (1992), 591-605.

5   Episodic memory involves stored information about specific events (e.g., 9/11), whereas semantic memory involves information that has general meaning and is not specific to any particular event (e.g., the geography of Afghanistan).

6   Rajesh Kasturirangan, "Thinking is Believing," *Progress in Brain Research* 168C (2007), 105-114.

7   Daniel Gilbert, "How Mental Systems Believe," *American Psychologist* 46 (1991), 107-119.

8   Folk psychology involves a set of shared social and/or cultural assumptions for explaining thinking, behaviour and the causal links between them.

9   Bertram Malle and Joshua Knobe, "The Distinction Between Desire and Intention: A Folk-Conceptual Analysis," in B.F. Malle, L.J. Moses and D.A. Baldwin, eds., *Intentions and Intentionality: Foundations of Social Cognition* (Cambridge: MIT Press, 2001), 45-67.

10   Alan Baddeley, *Working Memory, Thought and Action* (Oxford: Oxford University Press, 2007).

11   Joshua Knobe, "Intentional Action and Side Effects in Ordinary Language," *Analysis* 63 (2003), 190-193.

12   Ibid.

13   Joshua Knobe, "Theory of Mind and Moral Cognition: Exploring the Connections," *TRENDS in Cognitive Sciences* 9 (2005), 357-359.

14   Knobe, "Intentional Action," and Knobe, "Theory of Mind and Moral Cognition."

15   David Pizzaro, Eric Uhlmann and Peter Salovey, "Asymmetry in Judgments of Moral Blame and Praise: The Role of Perceived Metadesires," *Psychological Science* 14 (2003), 267-272.

16   Knobe, "Theory of Mind and Moral Cognition."

17   Ibid.

18   Ibid.

19   Ibid.

20   Brooks King-Casas, Damon Tomlin, Cedric Anen, Colin Camerer, Steven Quartz and Read Montague, "Getting to Know You: Reputation and Trust in a Two-Person Economic Exchange," *Science* 308 (2005), 78-83.

21   The Ultimatum Game is a single-trial economic exchange game played anony-mously between two individuals. The trial starts by the first player proposing how to divide a sum of money. If the second player accepts the offer, the money is split according to the proposal. If the second player rejects the offer, neither player receives any money.

22   Ibid.

23   Dean Mobbs, Hakwan Lau, Owen Jones and Christopher Frith, "Law, Responsibility, and the Brain," *PLoS Biology* 5 (2007), 693-700.

24   Benjamin Libet, Curtis Gleason, Elwood Wright and Dennis Pearl, "Time of Conscious Intention to Act in Relation to Onset of Cerebral Activity (readiness-potential): The Unconscious Initiation of a Freely Voluntary Act," *Brain* 106 (1983), 623-642; Hakwan Lau, Robert Rogers and Richard Passingham, "On Measuring the Perceived Onsets of Spontaneous Actions," *Journal of Neuroscience* 26 (2006), 7265-7271; Hakwan Lau, Robert Rogers and Richard Passingham, "Manipulating the Experienced Onset of Intention After Action Execution," *Journal of Cognitive Neuroscience* 19 (2007), 81-90.

25   Daniel Dennett, *Consciousness Explained* (Boston: Little, Brown & Co., 1991).

26   Mobbs *et al.*, "Law, Responsibility, and the Brain."

27   Stephen Golding, Ronald Roesch and Jan Schreiber, "Assessment and Conceptualization of Competency to Stand Trial: Preliminary Data on the Interdisciplinary Fitness Review," *Law and Human Behavior* 8 (1984), 321-334.

28   Seena Fazel and John Danesh, "Serious Mental Disorder in 23,000 Prisoners: A Systematic Review of 62 Surveys," *Lancet* 359 (2002), 545-550.

29   Gollwitzer, "Implementation Intentions: Strong Effects of Simple Plans."

30   Baumeister, "Free Will in Scientific Psychology."

CHAPTER 4

Fostering Trust within Network-Enabled Operations: Challenges and Initial Recommendations

Sandra C. Hughes and Joan H. Johnston

NAVAL AIR WARFARE CENTRE TRAINING SYSTEMS DIVISION

INTRODUCTION

Proponents of Network-Centric Warfare (NCW) have embraced the notion that it will significantly enhance mission effectiveness by improving information sharing, collaboration and shared situational awareness. Since its inception, however, the United States' Joint Chiefs of Staff have raised significant concerns that implementing such network technologies will greatly increase the risk of miscommunication and misunderstanding.[1] For example, when networks are opened to users working under multinational conditions, the threat of erroneous interpretation can be exacerbated by different language standards and use of terminology. In addition, the lack of face-to-face social interaction can result in fewer social context cues (e.g., body language and paralinguistic characteristics).[2] Furthermore, compared to face-to-face groups, individuals working over networks tend to make more task-oriented statements, but make fewer social support statements such as expressing support or agreement.[3] Distributed collaboration groups also take longer to get oriented in the initial stages of a project.[4] Taken together, these findings indicate that quickly formed, fast moving teams working over networks may have a difficult time building and maintaining trusting interpersonal relationships.

NCW is built on the promise of improved information sharing. However, the people in the network must trust each other before they will be willing to share important information with one another.[5] Without trust, the potential of NCW will not be fully maximized. U.S. Rear-Admiral Thomas Zelibor highlighted this problem by stating that NCW is at a crossroads and that it demands a cultural shift from the typical military stance of "need to know" to "need to share." He also decried the emphasis on information security as something that could hinder operations: "We are too secure – we hoard information."[6]

In recent years, various nations have relabelled NCW with their own terms to assert that the human network is the priority and that network technologies should support it. Network-Enabled Operations (NEOps) is the term we selected that best represents the current perspective of the United States (e.g., the Unites States Office of Force Transformation, Office of Secretary of Defense), as well as that of NATO and many of our coalition partners.

In light of these concerns, research-based guidance is needed for fostering the influence of trust in human networks. We will therefore discuss the relevant research findings related to the individual and organizational factors that affect trust building and provide implications for building trust in NEOps. It is beyond the scope of this chapter to conduct a comprehensive review of the trust literature, so the reader is therefore referred to key references that can expand their understanding of particular topics.

BACKGROUND

The principle aim of NEOps is to acquire information superiority, speed of command, and rapid, decisive targeting by employing a distributed, network-centric coalition force.[7] Its original proponents drew upon decades of learning from the successes and failures of networked systems employed by military forces (e.g., U.S. Navy carrier battle groups and U.S. Air Force air combat operations).

What sets NEOps apart is that networked systems will be employed in a way that is fundamentally different from how they are used today. A single person or even a small network of teams will no longer accomplish all mission tasks. Instead, mission success will be founded on a complete redesign of military organizations and doctrine. Multiple networks of teams will interlink to carry out command intent through extensive information sharing.[8] A much larger distributed total force will be created, from soldiers to coalition force capabilities to strategic commands.

The increased number and diversity of individuals, groups and multiple teams available and communicating through information networks will improve decision-making processes, but fewer people will be required to effect mission success because temporary teams composed of just the right people to get the job done will be used. As extensive face-to-face interactions and formal reporting hierarchies disappear, improved mission success will be achieved from decentralized decision-making.[9] Greater dependence among the actors is expected; no one person will have all the information available in the network and it will need to be shared. Ideally, better quality and increased information sharing will lead to increased collaboration, resulting in better, shared situational awareness.

Before moving to a discussion of research on trust, and how to engender it in a NEOps environment, we will discuss the United States' concept of command intent and its relationship to trust. The United States Army includes command intent within its basic doctrine for operations. The 1993 Army Field Manual (FM) 100-5 defines it as a concise expression of the purpose of an operation and a description of the desired end-state.[10] Its purpose is to focus subordinates on what has to be accomplished in order to achieve success. Thus, instead of telling them how to accomplish the overarching goal, it communicates the desired *effects*. Commander's intent is a joint doctrine in the United States. The Joint Chiefs of Staff have embraced it as an essential tool to coordinate diverse military forces, especially at the operational level of war.[11] The concept of command intent has become prominent in discussion of network-centric warfare, due to its focus on decentralized decision-making. If command intent is effectively conveyed and understood, leadership at lower levels can take the right action based on local knowledge without direct orders from above: self-synchronization can occur. This efficient activity is called "power to the edge." If the behaviours occur without extensive oversight from the military hierarchy, it is referred to as "self-synchronization." Self-synchronization will increase the speed of command; actions will be taken so quickly that enemies will have limited time to react.[12] Trust in information, subordinates, superiors, peers and equipment is necessary for self-synchronization to occur.[13]

Command intent and trust are related in several ways. Trust is required in order to implement the concept of command intent and "power to the edge." Leaders must trust their followers to translate broad mission plans into actionable steps.[14] This requires that commanders must have a degree of trust that their subordinates are competent, predictable and have goals consistent with their own. Further, when a leader demonstrates trust in subordinates, they feel empowered and encouraged to take the risks necessary to implement command intent. Followers must trust their leaders in order to accept and commit to command intent. They must see their leaders as trustworthy in order to accept their decisions and guidance.[15]

We see trust as a requirement for implementing command intent. Conversely, shared command intent may enhance trust among all members of a team. If followers understand and commit to implementing command intent, then we can say that they have shared command intent or common intent. Just as team members will perform more effectively when they have shared mental models (overlapping knowledge about each other and the situation), they will perform better if they share the same goals. Trust is also enhanced when goals are shared, in part because congruent goals allow people to predict how others will act and what information needs to be shared.

The NEOps perspective relies heavily on culturally diverse individuals, groups and teams interacting with each other to perform complex tasks, distributed in both space and time. These factors taken together characterize the context in which command intent is expected to be communicated and trust is developed. In the next section we discuss the relevant trust research in the context of these NEOps factors to gain a better understanding of the implications for fostering trust.

TRUST RESEARCH

Social exchange theory has shaped the development of trust research. It proposes that people are more likely to work together if they reinforce each other's behaviours (reciprocity) through socially accepted practices, trust, and the willingness to take risks. When individuals learn to trust one another, they are able to rely on generalized forms of reciprocity rather than on sequences of specific *quid pro quo* interactions.[16] It allows them to achieve far more than when these forms of "social capital" are not present. Investments made in one time period in building trust and reciprocity can produce higher levels of return in future time periods, even though the individuals involved are not necessarily consciously trying to construct social capital.[17] In the military setting, reciprocity forms the foundation for trust between commanders and their subordinates and is considered critical to executing command intent.

As a result of the importance of this relationship, this chapter is focused on understanding how trust is established. Figure 4-1 presents an input-process-outcome model showing that behavioural outcomes (risk taking and job performance) result from the formation of trust, which is founded on individual (e.g., cognitions and dispositions) and organizational (e.g., climate, team dynamics and diversity) factors. In this context, the development of trust is a decision process and many definitions and measures of trust have been developed to characterize it.[18] Researchers have sought to develop a definition of trust that removes references to what are known as its precursors (e.g., trustworthiness) and outcomes (e.g., risk taking) to better understand how cognitions affect behaviours.[19]   In Colquitt, Scott and LePine's meta-analysis, measures of trust were selected based on whether items assessed an "intention to accept vulnerability" and having "positive expectations" about the trustee.[20] Trust has also been defined as "the willingness of a party to be vulnerable to the outcomes of another party based on the expectation that the other will perform a particular action important to the trustor, irrespective of the ability to monitor or control that other party."[21] Trust has also been defined as "a psychological state comprising the intention to accept vulnerability based upon positive expectations of the intentions or behaviour of another."[22]

INDIVIDUAL FACTORS

The main cognitive factor for fostering trust is confidence that the other person is competent and predictable. There is strong empirical support for the need to develop positive thoughts and feelings of trustworthiness towards the trustee before trust can occur.[23] Perceptions of trustworthiness include beliefs about the trustee's competence and integrity and how much the trustee is concerned about the trustor's welfare (benevolence).[24]

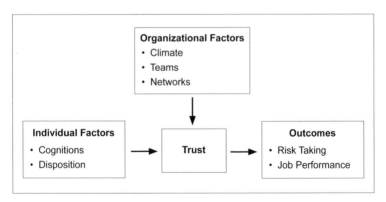

Figure 4-1: Model of Factors.

Interactions in distributed tasks may also be affected by propensity to trust. "Trust propensity" describes a stable individual difference variable, which affects the likelihood that a person will trust. Trust propensity is described as a generalized trust of others.[25] Individuals who have a high trust propensity extend trust, appear to be trustworthy, and thus engender trust, leading to a continuous trust cycle. The authors noted that these types of interactions are probably most critical during the initial stages of a group's work. The need for at least a minimum level of propensity towards trust seems especially critical in situations where one does not have time to develop a close, personal relationship with individuals and groups that need to be trusted.

ORGANIZATIONAL FACTORS

A collaborative climate is an important organizational factor found to significantly affect developing perceptions of trustworthiness. Research has shown that leaders must entrust team members with meaningful levels of responsibility, provide them with the necessary autonomy to achieve results, present challenging opportunities which stretch the individual abilities of team members, and recognize and reward superior performance. In particular, military leaders can influence trust if they establish a climate in which they demonstrate a reasoned willingness to allow people to take risks. Leaders who establish a supportive and collaborative environment encouraging some degree of risk-taking, empower team members to exhibit a bias for action, which in turn creates an enthusiasm and commitment to the team's goals.[26] The magnitude of the importance of trust in leadership is reflected by the tremendous investment the international military establishment has made in development programs that train and mentor the skills that create a supportive decision-making climate. For example, the Canadian Forces advise that effective leaders build and maintain trust by demonstrating competence; showing care and consideration for others; demonstrating character (integrity, dependability and fairness); showing consideration and respect for subordinates; demonstrating concern for the well-being of subordinates; and avoiding exposing them to unnecessary risks.[27]

A second key organizational factor is that of team dynamics; team members must understand and commit to command intent in order to develop shared command intent (common intent). This process may be complicated by the nature of NEOps team dynamics, which are often *ad hoc*, highly interdependent, distributed and diverse. Following is an exploration of each of these areas.

Ad hoc **teams.** One of the benefits of NEOps is that it allows for the rapid formation of a team to meet a specific objective. Teams can be composed of members with just the right combination of expertise and skills to get the job done. Once the objective has been met, the team may be dissolved. The need for trust often arises when the trustor lacks complete information about the trustee's ability, benevolence or integrity.[28] When teams are rapidly composed to meet specific requirements, there is a great likelihood that people who have not worked together in the past will be expected to complete a task, working as a coordinated team.

Trust is typically developed through face-to-face social process over time through shared experiences, observations and interactions;[29] it is not something that can be ordered. The competence component of trust usually develops when members show themselves trustworthy by communicating openly, following through with commitments and acting effectively. Social exchanges over time may provide the affective "glue" that brings it all together. The need to get *ad hoc* teams "up to speed" in short order represents a key challenge.

Dependence. The need for trust varies according to task type: some tasks simply require more trust than others. For example, high levels of trust are required when participants must negotiate complex agreements.[30] However, high levels of trust may not be needed for brainstorming tasks. It has also been argued that there is an optimal level of trust in each situation and that the more interdependency there is between exchange partners (or team-mates), the more trust is required in order to achieve efficiency and not to miss opportunities for improvement.[31] In highly interdependent tasks, trust contributes to developing effective teamwork by allowing members to stay problem-focused, promoting more efficient communication and coordination, and encouraging compensation behaviours whereby a member picks up the slack that occurs when another member falters.[32]

Distribution. Development of the personal relationships that lead to trust is hindered in a distributed environment because of the lack of physical proximity, face-to-face interactions, opportunities for social exchange and discussion, and nonverbal behaviours.[33] Remote teams have less trust at the outset than face-to-face teams and they have more difficulties developing trust over time. Even when such exchanges do occur, they usually lack the vividness and intensity of face-to-face exchanges.[34] People can also become more "self-absorbed versus other-oriented" when they interact via computer-mediated communication mechanisms because they have less social context information.[35] In addition, in the realm of distance learning via computer-mediated communication technologies, anonymity has led to increased cheating, reneging and extreme language; all behaviours that would lead to diminished trust.[36]

Therefore, fostering trust in distributed teams requires a focus on initial interactions to develop shared goals. If a team has members working together for the first time or who will be working in a distributed setting, then initial face-to-face meetings at the kick-off and at critical decision points in a task are advised. If face-to-face interactions are not possible, then video-teleconferencing (VTC) technologies should be used. Several studies have shown that trust can be built quickly with this technology, provided that participants engage in getting-acquainted activities.[37]

During initial discussions, it is important to establish that all parties are talking about the same thing and that they are all committed to the same goal.[38] Shared reference materials can provide an organizing frame of reference for the group to discuss. Early communications should examine assumptions and establish common vocabularies. For example, groupware (programs that help people work together collectively while located remotely from each other) could provide prompts to guide a group discussion on command intent. Having the system explicitly question various groups as to their understanding of command intent might encourage clarifying discussions.

Socialization processes have been found to be important to fostering trust in distributed teams. The more "points of contact" people have with one another, the better they are able to predict one another's behaviour.[39] Biographies or résumés could be shared, thereby enhancing understanding of an unknown team member's competence. Social networking applications can be used to create networks based on shared interests and work responsibilities and to create a joint name, title or logo. These applications support "blogs," posting personal information (e.g., profiles, professional interests and educational background), shared links, discussion forums and document management.[40] The challenge is to avoid the time-wasting components while leveraging the collaborative potential.[41] Many organizations have blocked access to such tools because of the potential for sharing too much company information or wasting time.

Similar to ratings on the Internet of an individual's reputation for following through on delivering a quality product on time and at low cost, individuals in NEOps could create "reputation scores."[42] An individual could build his/her own reputation by having an established visual record on a webpage that presents levels of satisfaction in his/her performance and in his/her ability to foster trust through feedback from satisfied team members. Similarly, trust could be nurtured by establishing a webpage that presents his/her combined reputation based on team member contributions. Like a sports team, a reputation could be built and advertised quickly if reaction data is collected at the team's inception.

Diversity. In global virtual teams, personnel must work together, even though their affiliations cut across functions, organizations and geography.[43] Social identity theory suggests that people who view themselves as similar to one another are more likely to trust one another. Category-based or presumptive trust is based on a person's membership in a group or category (reputation) that people have come to trust or from shared membership in a group to which they belong.[44] This type of trust is conferred on people with no history of direct personal contact. In contrast, members of diverse teams may be forced to deal with unfamiliar processes, environments and expectations (of themselves and others).[45] Furthermore, a diverse team will not be able to rely on interpersonal similarity and common backgrounds and experiences to produce mutual attraction and a willingness to work cooperatively.[46] For example, issues related to trust have emerged between coalition members of different nationalities working together in the Middle East. A study of Australian Defence Force personnel reported that trust was cited as a critical factor in U.S./Australian cooperation, especially as it related to information sharing.[47] An individual's ability to get information strongly depends on the relationships he or she can tap into. When deployed in the Middle East, Australians realized early that unless they fostered good relationships with the Americans, they would not be able to receive the required information. The most effective way for an Australian to build trust with an American was to engage in off-duty socializing. This process was hindered because developing one-on-one relationships usually depended on individual initiative, and whenever coalition mission personnel were rotated out, the process of fostering trust had to start all over again.

Establishing a collective identity bolsters identity-based trust and creates joint goals or objectives that are relevant when a diverse group is working together.[48] The global virtual teams research indicates that training should be developed to help individuals learn how to facilitate trust within a multicultural team as it matures.[49] Steps taken early in a team's establishment should focus on social exchanges, communications conveying enthusiasm, coping with technical and task uncertainty, taking initiative and volunteering. Later behaviours that facilitate trust include predictable and regular patterns of communication, warning of absences, substantive and timely responses (explicit and prompt responses that messages were read and evaluated), rotating leadership among members, transitioning from rules to emphasis on the task and calm reaction to crisis.

IMPLICATIONS FOR NEOps

The research described above suggests that if the supporting methods, training and technologies are available, individuals may develop competencies for fostering trust in order to adapt to rapidly formed teams, dependence, distribution and diversity. However, it is not certain that the strategies will transfer to fostering trust in NEOps because the findings were focused primarily on individual and single team relationships, in face-to-face or distributed environments. NEOps implies a more complex interaction of factors that are confounded in the current research designs; it is difficult to determine which factors may have more influence. The following is a description of research that exemplifies how the various factors of distribution combined with disposition, time and dependence, and team composition, may interact to affect trust performance outcomes.

In high-risk and high-stakes tasks, and when time was short, team members developed the willingness to suspend doubt about whether or not strangers could be counted on in order to get to work on the group's tasks. In essence they developed "swift trust."[50] Researchers discovered that such groups are tied together by a form of trust with the following properties: the belief/hope that others will care for what is being entrusted with good will; willingness to suspend doubt in order to execute the task performance; willingness to take risk; and, a positive expectation of benefits of temporary group activity. It has also been reported that establishing swift trust at the beginning of an online course appears to be related to subsequent course success.[51]

Finally, group dynamics theory suggests that information sharing could be negatively affected among networked groups.[52] For example, members of heterogeneous military teams were found to have increased uncertainty and to make biased decisions based on perceptions about the motives and actions of others. Several experiments have been conducted examining patterns of information trust in the context of a military sense-making task embedded in a simulated coalition engagement. In the first experiment, researchers found that user awareness of a message source (and any assumptions or biases associated with that) had an overriding influence on their decision to trust or not to trust the information it contained, regardless of information quality.[53] In a follow-up study, it was found that teams actually made better information trust/distrust judgments with anonymous sources.[54] The researchers postulated that individuals paid closer attention to the quality of the information when the source was unknown.

In the context of these findings, a program of research is needed to systematically evaluate the impact of multiple factors on trust. An important factor is the *time* needed to develop trust, but it has been ignored as a potentially serious issue that could be greatly affected by NEOps. In NEOps, the emphasis on speed of command through rapid formation of *ad hoc* teams with changing leaders is likely to have a significant impact on fostering trust.

Table 4-1 presents an example framework for specifying hypotheses on how trust might be fostered given such factors as time, dependence, distribution and diversity. The first column lists the critical research topic: Fostering trust in leadership. The second column presents a specific research question for that topic: How will trust be fostered when a less experienced and more junior officer has to lead people in accomplishing tasks? In traditional military organizations, military leaders are typically older and more experienced than their subordinates and have built a reputation over a long period of time. However, the "Edge Organization" concept relies heavily on empowering individuals at all levels of the organization to make decisions. In essence, everyone has the chance to lead. Another key challenge is that the ability to develop person-based trust through direct interactions will no longer be the norm. A critical requirement will be to understand mechanisms that will facilitate trust when "unproven" team members must execute leader responsibilities. Therefore, Table 4-1 presents research-based hypotheses for each of the major NEOps factors (i.e., time, dependence, distribution and diversity) in the remaining columns. In the third column, it is proposed that when time is available, building a reputation for competence and integrity with others will foster trust. If time is short, fostering "swift trust" among team members will be more effective. The fourth column proposes that fostering trust among team members will be more effective if the team has high task interdependence, otherwise leaders will be more effective if they foster trust with individual team members. The fifth column proposes that using a webpage to rapidly advertise a leader's skills will help to more rapidly build his or her reputation. The sixth column proposes that leaders will be more effective in fostering trust in multicultural teams if they enable team members to focus on validating the information they need, rather than the national origin of the information source.

Research Topic	Research Question	Time	Dependence	Distribution	Diversity
Fostering trust in leadership.	How will trust be fostered when a less experienced and more junior officer has to lead people in accomplishing tasks?	If there is time, trust will be fostered by building a reputation of competence and integrity with others. If time is short, then fostering "swift trust" among team members will be effective.	Fostering trust among team members will be more effective if the team has high task interdependence, otherwise leaders will be more effective if they foster trust with individual team members.	Using a webpage to rapidly advertise a leader's reputation will help to more rapidly foster trust.	Leaders will be effective in fostering trust in multicultural teams if they enable team members to focus on validating the information they need, rather than information sources

Table 4-1: Example Framework for Specifying Hypotheses about Fostering Trust in NEOps.

RECOMMENDATIONS

In order to implement the construct of command intent, where subordinates take initiative without explicit direction from above, a climate of trust between leaders and followers throughout the networked team is necessary. As we have discussed, the NEOps environment may be a challenging place to develop trust. In light of the above discussions, it is postulated that extensive research requiring considerable investment of time, money, resources and international cooperation is needed. In the near term, we recommend a mission analysis of NEOps to identify the range of missions and resulting tasks that are most influenced by the need to foster trust. Then, the critical knowledge, skills, abilities and other personal characteristics required for fostering trust can be derived with a goal of identifying the most critical gaps that need research. A systematic approach that specifies important research studies will produce validated demonstrations and sound design guidelines for fostering trust in the human network. From this, the methods, tools and strategies that should be enabled via NEOps technologies will emerge.

ENDNOTES

1   Joint Chiefs of Staff, *Joint Publication 6-0: Doctrine for Command, Control, Communications, and Computers (C4) System Support in Joint Operations* (Washington, D.C.: U.S. Government Printing Office, May 1995), II-9.

2   Lee Sproull and Sara Kiesler, "Reducing Social Context Cues: Electronic Mail in Organizational Communications," *Management Science* 32, 11 (1986), 1492-1512.

3   S. Hiltz, M. Turoff and K. Johnson, "Experiments in Group Decision Making: Disinhibition, Deindividuation, and Group Process in Pen and Real Name Computer Conferences," *Decision Support Systems* 5 (1989), 217-232.

4   S. Hughes, J. Driskell and R. Willis, "Distributed Team Decision-Making," Unpublished Technical Report, Naval Air Warfare Center, Training Systems Division, Orlando, FL, 1994.

5   G. Fine and L. Holyfield, "Secrecy, Trust, and Dangerous Leisure: Generating Group Cohesion in Voluntary Organizations," *Social Psychology Quarterly* 59, 1 (1996), 22-38.

6   Rear-Admiral T.E. Zelibor, USN, Director of Global Operations, U.S. Strategic Command, "Network-Centric Operations: Balancing Speed and Agility with Security," *Armed Forces Communication and Electronics Association (AFCEA) TechNet International Annual Conference and Exposition*, Washington, D.C., May 2005.

7   David Alberts and Richard Hayes, *Power to the Edge: Command...Control... in the Information Age.* Command and Control Research Program Publications. Retrieved 4 September 2007 from http://www.dodccrp.org/publications/pdf/ Alberts_Power.pdf.

8   Nicole Blatt, "Trust and Influence in the Information Age: Operational Requirements for Network Centric Warfare" (Unpublished Master's thesis, Naval Postgraduate School, Monteray, CA). Retrieved 29 January 2008 from http://stinet. dtic.mil/dticrev/PDFs/ADA429673.pdf.

9   Alberts and Hayes, *Power to the Edge.*

10   United States Army, FM-1005, Field Manual on Operations, Headquarters, Department of the United States Army. Retrieved 20 February 2008 from http:// www.fs.fed.us/fire/doctrine/genesis_and_evolution/source_materials/FM-100-5_ operations.pdf. The United States Army generally uses "Command Intent" to refer to the construct of Command Intent. However, we use "Command Intent" to be consistent with practices of our international partners.

11   Lieutenant-Colonel Michael Straight, USAF, "Commander's Intent: An Aerospace Tool for Command and Control?" *Air Power Journal* (Spring 1996). Retrieved 20 February 2007 from http://www.airpower.maxwell.af.mil/airchronicles/ apj/apj96/spr96/straight.pdf.

12   Arthur Cebrowski and John Garstka, "Network-Centric Warfare: Its Origin and Future," *Proceedings of the Naval Academy* 124, 1 (1998), 28-35.

13   Alberts and Hayes, *Power to the Edge.*

14   Barbara Adams, David Bryant and Robert Webb, "Trust in Teams Literature Review," Department of National Defence Report N. CR-2001-042 (2001).

82

15   Tom Tyler and Peter Degoey, "Trust in Organizational Authorities: The Influence of Motive Attributions on Willingness to Accept Decisions," in R.M. Kramer and T.R. Tyler, eds., *Trust in Organizations: Frontiers of Theory and Research* (Thousand Oaks, CA: Sage Publications, 1996), 114-139.

16   Elinor Ostrom, as cited in Partha Dasgupta and Ismail Serageldin, *Social Capital: A Multifaceted Perspective* (Washington, D.C.: World Bank Organization, 1999).

17   Alberts and Hayes, *Power to the Edge*.

18   Shawn Burke, Dana Sims, Elizabeth Lazzara and Edvardo Salas, "Trust in Leadership: A Multi-level Review and Integration," *The Leadership Quarterly* 18 (2007), 606-632.

19   J.A. Colquitt, B.A. Scott and J.A. LePine, "Trust, Trustworthiness and Trust Propensity: A Meta-analytic Test of their Unique Relationships with Risk Taking and Job Performance," *Journal of Applied Psychology* 92, 4 (2007), 909-927.

20   Ibid., 909.

21   Roger Mayer, James Davis and David Schoorman, "An Integrative Model of Organizational Trust," *The Academy of Management Review* 20, 3 (1995), 712.

22   Denise Rosseau, B. Sitkin, Ronald Burt and Colin Camerer, "Not so Different After All: A Cross-Discipline View of Trust," *Academy of Management Review* 23, 3 (1998), 395.

23   Colquitt, Scott and LePine, "Trust, Trustworthiness and Trust Propensity."

24   S. Jarvenpaa and T.R. Shaw, "Global Virtual Teams: Integrating Models of Trust, Organizational Virtualness," in P. Sieber and J. Griese, eds., *Proceedings of the V O Net – Workshop* (Bern: Simowa Verlag, April 1998), 35-51.

25   Colquitt, Scott and LePine, "Trust, Trustworthiness and Trust Propensity."

26   Carl Larson and Frank Lafasto, *Teamwork: What Must go Right / What Can go Wrong* (Newbury Park, CA: Sage Publications, 1989).

27   Canada, Department of National Defence, *Leadership in the Canadian Forces: Conceptual Foundations* (Ottawa: DND, 2007).

28   Roger Mayer, James Davis and David Schoorman, "An Integrative Model of Organizational Trust," *The Academy of Management Review* 20, 3 (1995), 709-734.

29   Blatt, "Trust and Influence in the Information Age."

30   Elinor Ostrom, James Walker and Roy Gardner, "Trust Without Touch: Jumpstarting Long-Distance Trust with Initial Social Activities," in Jun Zheng, Elizabeth Veinott, Nathan Bos, Judith Olson and Gary Olson, eds., *Proceedings of CHI 2002* (New York: ACM Press, 1992).

31   Andrew Wicks, Shawn Berman and Thomas Jones, "The Structure of Optimal Trust: Moral and Strategic Implications," *Academy of Management Review* 24, 1 (1999), 99-116.

32   Kimberly Smith-Jentsch, Rhonda Zeisig, Bruce Acton and James McPherson, "Team Dimensional Training," in J.A. Cannon-Bowers and E. Salas, eds., *Making Decisions Under Stress: Implications for Individual and Team Training* (Washington, D.C.: American Psychological Association, 1998), 271-297. See also Larson and Lafasto, *Teamwork*.

33   K.G. Brown and M.E. Van Buren, "Applying a Social Capital Perspective to the Evaluation of Distance Training," in S.M. Fiore and E. Salas, eds., *Toward a Science of Distributed Learning* (Washington, D.C.: American Psychological Association, 2007). See also M. Lea and R. Spears, "Love at First Byte? Building Personal Relationships over Computer Networks," in J.T. Wood and S. Duck, eds., *Understudied Relationships: Off the Beaten Track* (Thousand Oaks, CA: Sage, 1995), 197-233. See also, Gary Olson and Judith Olson, "Distance Matter," *Human Computer Interaction* 15 (2000), 139-179.

34   Brown and Van Buren, "Applying a Social Capital Perspective."

35   Sproull and Kiesler, "Reducing Social Context Cues."

36   Robert Putnam, as cited in Brown and Van Buren, "Applying a Social Capital Perspective."

37   Nathan Bos, Judith Olson, Darren Gergle, Gary Olson and Zach Wright, "Effects of Four Computer-Mediated Communications Channels on Trust Development," *Proceedings of the SIGCHI Conference on Human Factors in Computing Systems* (2002), 135-140.

38   Roy Lewicki and Barbara Bunker, "Developing and Maintaining Trust in Work Relationships," in R.M. Kramer and T.R. Tyler, eds., *Trust in Organizations: Frontiers of Theory and Research* (Thousand Oaks, CA: Sage Publications, 1996), 114-139.

39   Blair Sheppard and Marla Tuchinsky, "Interfirm Relationships: A Grammar of Pairs," in L.L. Cummings and B.M. Staw, eds., *Research in Organizational Behavior* (Greenwich, CT: JAI Press, 1996), Vol. 18, 331-373.

40   J.N. Hoover, "Social Experiment," *Information Week,* 24 September 2007, 40-47.

41   Ibid.

42   Blatt, "Trust and Influence in the Information Age."

43   Jarvenpaa and Shaw, "Global Virtual Teams."

44   Adams, Bryant and Webb, "Trust in Teams Literature Review."

45   C. Lewis, "Managing and Working with Diverse Teams." Retrieved 28 August 2007 from http://www.allpm.com/modules.php?op=modload&name=News&file=article&sid=1514&mode=thread&order=0&thold=0.

46   Ellen Berscheid and Elaine Walster, *Interpersonal Attraction,* 2nd Ed. (Reading, MA: Addison Wesley, 1978).

47   Irene Ali, "Is NCW Information Sharing a Double Edged Sword? – Voices from the Battlespace," Integrated Capabilities Branch, Defence Systems Analysis Division, DSTO Fernhill, Department of Defence. Retrieved 2 February 2008 from http://www.dsto.defence.gov.au/attachments/Ali_Is%20NCW%20Information%20Sharing%20a%20Double%20Edged%20Sword%20-%20Voices%20from%20the%20Battlespace.pdf.

48   Lewicki and Bunker, "Developing and Maintaining Trust in Work Relationships."

49   S. Jarvenpaa and Dorothy Leidner, "Communication and Trust in Global Virtual Teams," *Organization Science* 10, 6 (1999), 791-815.

50   Debra Meyerson, Karl Weick and Roderick Kramer, "Swift Trust and Temporary Groups," in R.M. Kramer and T.R. Tyler, eds., *Trust in Organizations: Frontiers of Theory and Research* (Thousand Oaks, CA: Sage Publications, 1996).

51   N.W. Coppola, S.R. Hiltz and N. Rotter, "Building Trust in Virtual Teams," *IEEE Transactions on Professional Communications* 47, 2 (2004), 97-104.

52   D.M. McCallum, K. Harring, R. Gilmore, S. Drenan, J.P. Chase, C.A. Insko and J. Thibaut, "Competition and Cooperation Between Groups and Between Individuals," *Journal of Experimental Social Psychology* 21 (1985), 301-320.

53   Barry McGuinness and Andrew Leggatt, "Information Trust and Distrust in a Sensemaking Task," *Command and Control Research and Technology Symposium* (San Diego: Department of Defence Command & Control Research Program, 2006).

54   Andrew Leggatt and Barry McGuinness, "Factors Influencing Information Trust and Distrust in a Sensemaking Task," *11ᵗʰ International Command and Control Research and Technology Symposium* (Cambridge, UK: Defence Command & Control Research Program, 2006).

CHAPTER 5

Measurement of Intent: A Selective Review of the Literature

Keith Stewart

DEFENCE RESEARCH AND DEVELOPMENT CANADA – TORONTO

> *Mission Command ... has three enduring tenets: the importance of understanding a superior commander's intent, a clear responsibility to fulfil that intent, and timely decision-making. The underlying requirement is the fundamental responsibility to act within the framework of the commander's intentions.*

Canadian Forces Publication 300(3), *Command*.[1]

INTRODUCTION

In their definition of command and control, Ross Pigeau and Carol McCann emphasise that coordinated action is dependent upon the establishment of common intent, which they define as "the sum of shared explicit intent plus operationally relevant shared implicit intent."[2] In the same paper, they define intent as "an aim or purpose along with all of its associated connotations."[3] In a later publication, they stress that, "intent includes an explicit portion that contains the stated objective ... and an implicit portion that remains unexpressed for reasons of expediency but nonetheless is assumed to be understood."[4] The extent to which a commander will provide explicit direction to subordinates is dependent upon a range of factors including organisational culture and command philosophy, experience, training and the risk inherent in the specific situation that the orders are designed to address. I discuss these factors in a separate paper where I also consider how military organisations might develop flexibility in their approach to command based upon the balance between explicit and implicit intent.[5]

Lars Groth observed that humans with shared or compatible purpose organise in order to accomplish tasks that are not within the capacity of individuals acting independently.[6] Organisation, according to Henry Mintzberg, comprises the division of labour into distinct tasks and co-ordination between those tasks.[7] Since coordinated action is central to the success of collaborative endeavour, it follows that achieving an appropriate degree of common intent is a necessary, although not sufficient, precursor to success. In view of this, it is reasonable for those concerned with understanding how to optimise collaborative performance to seek to assess the extent to which common intent is achieved. This chapter reviews studies that have attempted to measure the success of the intent transmission process to the extent that it promotes compatibility of intent between commanders and their subordinates. The focus of this specific discussion is primarily methodological, although some discussion of intent theory is included where appropriate.

COMPARING COMPATIBILITY OF SUPER AND SUBORDINATE COMMANDER'S INTENT (CI)

This chapter reviews eight studies that incorporated methods for assessing the compatibility of subordinate commanders' intent with that of their superiors. A brief review of each of these studies is provided below. It is noted that, while similar terms are used to describe the aims of the studies, the investigators sometimes appear to be examining subtly different aspects of intent. It is possible that these are, in part, indicative of differences in command philosophy, specifically, the tendency to view a statement of intent as guidance to elicit a particular form of solution as opposed to an indication of a boundary for subordinates to work within.

In a study by Lawrence Shattuck,[8] 16 U.S. Army company commanders were required to develop orders in response to battalion operation orders prepared by their respective commanders. They were then presented with two scenarios updating the tactical situation and asked to describe how they would respond. The battalion commanders, who had prepared the original orders with their staffs, were asked how they expected the company commanders to respond to the situation reports. They were then asked to compare their subordinates' responses relative to their own. Of the 32 company commander responses, battalion commanders judged that only 17 matched their intent. It appears that the judgment battalion commanders were asked to make was whether subordinates' responses matched their proposed course of action, not whether subordinates' responses were within the commander's intent (which could have allowed for a broader set of responses).

Shattuck reports that, following analysis of recordings of the company commanders verbalising their rationale, he discounted six of the 17 cases, even though battalion commanders reported the response to be in line with their own. Interestingly, he notes that in three of those six episodes, "although battalion commanders judged the decision of the company commanders to match their own, they were in fact substantially different. Battalion commanders considered them a match because the company commanders were 'thinking along the right lines.'"[9] This might indicate that battalion commanders recognised subordinates' responses to be within their intent, albeit not matching the anticipated course of action. Thus, assessment appears to have related to matches in the specific decision/course of action, rather than whether the proposal was within the commander's intent. It would be interesting to examine whether any of the 15 responses that did not match the course of action were, in fact, within the superior commander's intent, thus allowing a more optimistic reading of the experimental results. Certainly, this study seems to promote the view that the orders process should promote homogeneity of decision-making between echelons. For example, "imparting presence is the process of developing subordinates' decision-making framework so they would respond the same way the senior commanders would if they were able to view the situation through their eyes."[10] This variant of decentralised command promotes co-ordination; however, it has the potential to suppress subordinates' creativity within their broad appreciation of the commander's intent.

Shattuck's method might also have been used to assess the balance between explicit and implicit intent within the sample.[11] A comparison between the battalion orders and the responses proposed by the battalion commanders would have allowed an examination of the requirement on subordinates to draw upon their implicit intent in the specific circumstances described in the situation reports. It would be interesting to assess how the content of the company operations orders produced by subordinates varied in relation to the balance of explicit and implicit intent reflected in the battalion commanders' situation report responses.

A more recent paper by Geoffrey Hone, Ian Whitworth and Andy Farmilo describes the development of a, as yet untested, method for assessing the adequacy of intent transmission.[12] The authors describe a technique whereby a senior commander would assess the adequacy of orders produced by subordinate commanders one or two levels down (e.g., division – brigade – battalion). This assessment would entail only one question: "Do these orders use the available forces to best serve my intent?" Thus, there is no implication that subordinates are expected to produce any particular solution; the only requirement is that the commander's intent be satisfied.

Peter Murphy conducted a commander's intent study during the Australian Army's *Headline 2000* experiment. Participants included brigade commanders and their subordinate battle group commanders. As part of the study, one-sentence scenario snapshots were presented. These were within the context of the overall experiment, but described events that were not due to arise in the high fidelity scenario play. Participants were provided with four possible options for reaction and asked, independently, to rank these in terms of their appropriateness to CI.[13] Owing to the relatively small sample size, no formal analysis is provided. Nevertheless, Murphy's discussion of this part of his study is informative and demonstrates some of the variability in the teams' responses and their implications for operational effectiveness. In some cases, high levels of consistency were achieved between the commander and his team. In other cases, however, less effective patterns emerged. For example, in responding to one scenario, three subordinate commanders achieved a high degree of consensus between themselves, but their responses failed to coincide with that of their superior.

Andrew Leggatt sought to evaluate the effectiveness with which CI was promulgated through a distributed headquarters (HQ) during a large-scale experiment named Multinational Experiment 3 (MNE3).[14] The command organisation employed in this study was physically distributed at locations in several nations and depended upon network-based information and communications technology to support collaborative working. Moreover, the organisation was divided into a number of functional teams, for example, plans, logistics and knowledge management, with members of those teams being distributed across the various geographical locations. Consequently, both physical and organisational proximity were examined as independent variables in the study.

Over 100 participants responded independently to a set of probe statements by classifying them as either "true" or "false" in the context of the commander's intent. Statements were developed in co-operation with the exercise commander, a U.S. Marine Corps major-general who contributed to their wording. On each of the four days of the exercise, the commander selected six statements, from a larger pool of 15, for presentation to the participants.[15] In addition to rating the statements as either "true" or "false," participants were also asked to rate their confidence in their responses on a seven-point scale. The data generated were analysed using methods associated with signal detection theory to provide an assessment of participants' performance and bias.

In terms of classifying the statements as "true" or "false," analysis demonstrated no differences in performance between participants at different geographical locations except in the non-Anglophone nations where performance was significantly lower. The author of the study interprets this finding as representing a confounding effect of language. Interestingly, no differences were identified in terms of confidence. It may be useful to speculate further as to the precise nature of the apparent effect of language. It may be the case that participants had difficulties in understanding both the intent statement and the experimental probes. Alternatively, it is also possible that they misunderstood one or the other.[16] The confidence ratings may suggest that participants were unaware of any lack of understanding. It may also be the case that rather than misunderstanding, they were simply not able to achieve as extensive an understanding as Anglophone participants. This might imply difficulties for second language users in perceiving the implicit aspects of intent or aligning aspects of a new plan with their pre-existing tacit knowledge, values and attitudes. In a future study, an analysis of the explicit/implicit balance in the content of the probe statements would be useful. This would enable an examination of whether particular statements rely more heavily than others upon implicit aspects of intent for categorisation as true or false. It would also allow identification of any associated differences in performance on individual statements.

Those functional groups that were closer to the commander in organisational terms performed better than the other groups. A broadly similar pattern emerged in terms of confidence, with the highest performing functional team expressing most confidence. A more fine-grained analysis of performance shows no difference between the functional groups in their ability to identify true statements (i.e., those that were in line with the commander's intent). Differences were found, however, between functional groups in the extent to which false probes were identified and these, it seems, were central to the between-group difference in sensitivity. Leggatt's analysis suggests that the better performing functional groups adopted more conservative criteria, with a tendency to reject rather than accept probes that they were unsure about. Presumably this explains why their performance advantage was expressed in terms of sensitivity to false, rather than true, information. It seems fair to assume that when assessing statements that they found marginal, participants tended to choose "false," the more conservative answer. An interesting question is whether this difference is in any way associated with the balance of implicit/explicit intent expressed in the probe statements. It may be the case that judgments that "x is not what the commander wants" (i.e., correct rejection versus false alarm) are more dependent on the implicit aspects of intent than the explicit. It seems reasonable to argue that since commanders concentrate in orders on what they want rather than what they do not want, then the ability to identify false statements is dependent on an understanding of the implicit intent. Thus, more information on the nature of the false statements would be useful. It would be interesting to know whether false statements tended to describe specific "anti-goals" (which Gary Klein defines as "outcomes that are not desired") or rather whether there were statements reflecting low priority or irrelevant outcomes.[17] In view of the above, we might hypothesize that those functional groups that demonstrate a performance advantage are those that have a broader understanding of intent, specifically a deeper appreciation of the implicit aspects of intent. Since the functional groups in question were those closest to the commander in organisational terms, this might have developed as a result of a different quantity or quality of interaction with the commander and his immediate staff.

A variant of Leggatt's technique was employed by Jeffrey Thomas, Linda Pierce, Melissa Dixon and Gwenda Fong in a joint U.S.-Singapore command experiment.[18] An interesting element of this study was that the authors treated CI and situation awareness as equivalent concepts.[19] The probe statements are not reproduced in their paper, however, and thus it is not possible to assess whether they all dealt with CI or whether some presented purely situational information. The primary independent variable in the experiment was the level of technological support available to the command and control (C2) teams. In one condition, only basic support tools were provided ("non-interoperable"), and in the other condition, a more sophisticated suite of C2 tools was made available ("fully interoperable"). The basic hypothesis was that sensitivity would be greater for participants in the fully interoperable condition. Analysis of the experiment demonstrated a highly significant effect of condition on sensitivity, but not in the direction predicted. In fact, participants in the low interoperability condition performed better than those in the full interoperability condition. A number of possible reasons for this finding are discussed; perhaps the most telling comment is the refreshing observation that "…the findings from this report cautiously highlight the importance that additional technological capabilities are not solutions in and of themselves."[20]

Philip Farrell collected data during the same experiment as Leggatt (MNE3).[21] His specific focus was on the measurement of common intent, which he defined as the "combination of the explicit awareness or perception of Commander's Intent plus the implicit or internal expectation of Commander's Intent."[22] Farrell describes four methods that were used in MNE3 to examine the issue of intent. One of these relates to the probe statements described by Leggatt. This will be dealt with first.[23] Farrell indicated that the general consensus was that the statements did not sufficiently probe implicit intent. The analysis did not consider performance by functional or geographical grouping, but rather compared performance at different stages of the two-week experiment. Performance was consistent across the four days on which measurements were taken and demonstrated that participants judged statements to be true or false with 70 percent accuracy.[24]

Of the three other measures of common intent discussed by Farrell, two (measures based on direct observation of aspects of participants' behaviour and course corrections and interventions) were discounted owing to insufficient data. This should not be taken to indicate that these methods have no merit. Rather, on this occasion, features of the experimental environment meant that useful data could not be or were not collected. The fourth method described by Farrell focused on participants' perceptions of "action consistency" between the functional groups. Participants were asked to rate both the extent to which they believed other groups' actions were consistent with those of their own group and the extent to which they believed those actions were consistent with the commander's intent. It is proposed that participants' perceptions of action consistency provide an indirect measure of the degree of common intent (i.e., supporting Pigeau and McCann's assertion that the establishment of common intent enables co-ordinated action). Analysis was argued to show relatively low levels of common intent across the four days on which data were collected in terms of consistency with other groups and with the commander's intent. Although these results seem somewhat pessimistic, it should be remembered that currently no validated criterion measure of common intent exists, and consequently, stating what level of common intent is adequate is an arbitrary judgment. As such, further investigation of these measures would be very useful, in particular to address the question of how much commonality of intent is desirable and how this varies across organisations and situations.

Farrell and his colleagues conducted further measurements of common intent during Multinational Experiment 4 (MNE4).[25] Although the overall design and aims of MNE4 differed from MNE3, Farrell was able to develop the analytical techniques used in the previous experiment, including a novel approach based upon vector algebra.[26] Again, analyses focused on differences between the functional groups within the experimental HQ organisations (co-located and distributed). An assessment of the extent to which the various functional groups understood the commander's orders and guidance was made by conducting a survey of experimental observers and analysts several times during the course of the experiment. It was argued that this survey focused on explicit intent. Survey respondents were asked to make their assessments based on observation of the staff meetings that were conducted over the course of the experiment. Methodologically, it is interesting to consider the extent to which the data produced in this way are reliant upon the observers' appreciation of the orders and guidance. The validity and reliability of this criterion measure is worthy of further consideration. Moreover, since the assessment is based upon observations of participants' behaviour in meetings, there is a question as to the extent to which these data can be argued wholly to discount any effects of implicit intent, whether on the part of the experimental participants or the observers. These caveats notwithstanding, some interesting results were reported. In general, both the co-located and distributed HQs' understanding of orders and guidance (interpreted as explicit intent) improved over the course of the experiment with the co-located HQ assessed as having a higher level of understanding at five out of the six measurement points.

In this experiment, implicit intent was assessed based upon measurements of "action consistency" similar to those collected during MNE3. Action consistency is taken to be an indicator of both implicit intent and common intent. As in MNE3, participants (rather than observers) were asked to rate both the extent to which they believed that the actions of other groups within their own HQ were consistent with those of their own group and the extent to which they believed the actions of those other groups were consistent with the commander's intent. The results demonstrated a general increase in perceptions of action consistency across the three weeks of the study, which was interpreted as being indicative of the time required for implicit intent to be developed within HQs. Again, scores for the co-located HQ were higher than those for the distributed HQ. This is not entirely surprising since action consistency must be guided to some extent by explicit intent as well as implicit intent. Perhaps the most interesting finding here is the apparent consistency between findings derived from data generated by neutral observers and experimental participants. Farrell concludes by raising some interesting issues. One very important question concerns the issue of how much commonality of intent is necessary in order to optimise team performance. In addition, Farrell observes that further work is required in order to calibrate his measures of common intent so that they can be used reliably in different experiments and exercises.

The studies reviewed so far in this chapter have concentrated upon the measurement of various aspects of intent within command research and experimentation. Both Shattuck and Murphy suggested in their papers that their methods have the potential to support command training. This does appear plausible, however it should be stressed that effective training is dependent upon more than the availability of a valid and reliable tool for measuring the construct of interest. For example, unless new instructional content is introduced in the training environment, the training described would need to be based upon knowledge and skills developed earlier in the trainees' careers based on courses, doctrinal publications and standing operating procedures.

Recognising a lack of structured training for the interpretation, formulation and dissemination of intent, Jules Molloy et al. developed a prototype Commander's Intent Training Tool (ComITT).[27] During a ComITT session, trainees work in a computer-based training environment in a classroom setting. They are provided a scenario, developed by the ComITT trainer, and are asked to produce their own orders based upon those from a higher formation. To help them in this task, the software provides them with a text template to populate and a map that can be marked with appropriate symbols.

A training session with ComITT bears some resemblance to the experimental method described by Shattuck. Once the trainees have produced their initial orders, the scenario situation is updated and they are provided with an opportunity to update their orders in the light of the new information. Trainees are required to respond to two similar questionnaires during the course of the ComITT session. The first is presented once they have developed their first set of orders; the second when they have had an opportunity to make changes to their orders following the situation update. Example ComITT questions are reproduced in Table 5-1.

• How well did you understand the commander's intent?

• How confident are you that everyone else in your team interpreted the intent in the same way as you?

• From the commander's intent statement, what are your top three priorities at this time?

• From the commander's intent statement, what, if any, are your top three concerns at this time (e.g., any ambiguities, conflicting information, etc.)?

• What are your initial information requirements at this time?

• To what degree has your interpretation of the commander's intent altered in light of the situation update?

Table 5-1: Sample ComITT Questions.

The questions produced were not originally conceived as a measurement tool. Rather the purpose was to provide the trainer with information to structure a debriefing session. It is noted that the current ComITT prototype allows four individuals to undergo training at any one time. Thus the trainer has the opportunity to compare their responses to the questions, although, at present, no tools are provided for analysis beyond the ability to call up all the trainees' responses on one screen. Currently, therefore, the debriefing session is largely based on the trainer's subjective assessment of the trainees' responses. The software does not: support comparison of individuals' orders before and after the situation update; support comparison between the orders developed by different trainees; and/or, provide an automatic mechanism for comparing trainees' responses with a set solution. ComITT, therefore, does not provide a set of absolute performance standards or a set of measurement tools. Rather, the expertise of the trainer is relied upon in providing performance feedback and debriefing sessions appear to be based on eliciting information from participants as to their performance and relying upon this process to underpin learning.

Based upon formal feedback collected at a ComITT workshop, an exercise, and a demonstration at the Royal Military Academy Sandhurst, Molloy reports that, even in its prototype form, ComITT appears to provide trainees with a valuable experience. ComITT is currently the only tool of its type. Further development of this or similar systems, in line with sound training principles, has the potential to improve all aspects of the intent transmission process. Moreover, given the broad range of complex environments (full spectrum operations) that military personnel must operate in, there would appear to be an increasing requirement to support the achievement of common intent within our own forces. Training, perhaps more than any other line of capability development, including technology, seems to offer the most promising solution.

CONCLUSION

Studies that have addressed the measurement of commander's intent have been reviewed. All of the methods for analysis of CI that have been discussed have merit. Although it has not been stated previously in this discussion, it should be noted that each method has been designed to meet the opportunities and constraints of the environments in which the individual studies have been conducted. For the purposes of future command-related research, it is important to consider the types of applied questions that are likely to drive that work and to be prepared to deploy intent measures that enhance our understanding of the effects engendered by various independent variables. For example, in a network-enabled environment, one may wish to understand the effects of different communications modalities or different levels of familiarity between commander and subordinates. In the immediate future, such studies must also be conducted with a view to improving the available assessment tools in terms of validity and reliability. This also indicates a requirement for some criterion measure of intent to be developed. Moreover, by drawing on the intent process, it is possible to identify different dependent measures, for example, the degree to which intent is communicated as a function of subordinates' experience.

While there is no one accepted description of the stages that comprise the intent transmission process, it should be clear that within that process there is a requirement for subordinates to understand the commander's intent and then develop a course of action to satisfy that intent. Understanding of intent is necessary, but not sufficient, for the development of an appropriate course of action. From the researcher's point of view, development of a suitable course of action provides some indication that intent has been understood; however, as Shattuck discovered when he analysed decision-makers' verbal protocols, it is quite possible for subordinates to generate a "correct" response without fully understanding the commander's intent. Conversely, an inability to develop an appropriate course of action cannot be taken to imply a lack of understanding of intent.

The key questions for the researcher are first, do subordinates understand what is and what is not the commander's intent, and second, can they tell which courses of action are within the boundaries of intent and which are not.[28] The intent probes method used by Leggatt and Farrell in their studies broadly satisfies these criteria. It has the advantage that it allows the researcher to take soundings across the entire space of potential solutions, examining participants' understanding of what is and what is not intent. Moreover, by varying the content of the probe statements, researchers could potentially assess subordinates' ability to make such judgments based upon variations in the levels of implicit and explicit intent. This is an important issue and one that both Farrell and Leggatt recognised to be worthy of further attention. Although Leggatt observed that the probe statements used in his study contained elements of both implicit and explicit intent, and saw a balance of both "true" and "false" statements, no formal analysis of these variables is reported. It is proposed that in a future study, these variables should be systematically varied with a view to strengthening the intent measures toolset.

ENDNOTES

1   Canada, *Command*, Canadian Forces Publication 300(3), B-GL-300-003/FP-000 (1996), 30.

2   Ross Pigeau and Carol McCann, "Redefining Command and Control," in Carol McCann and Ross Pigeau, eds., *The Human in Command* (New York: Plenum Press, 2000), 172. Pigeau and McCann define command and control as the "establishment of common intent to achieve coordinated action."

3   Ibid., 165.

4   Ross Pigeau and Carol McCann, "Establishing Common Intent: The Key to Co-ordinated Military Action," in Allan D. English, ed., *The Operational Art: Canadian Perspectives – Leadership and Command* (Kingston: Canadian Defence Academy Press, 2006), 91.

5   Keith Stewart, "Mission Command: Elasticity, Equilibrium, Culture and Intent," DRDC TR 2006-254 (2006).

6   Lars Groth, *Future Organizational Design: The Scope for the IT-based Enterprise* (New York: John Wiley & Sons, 1999).

7   Henry Mintzberg, *The Structuring of Organizations: A Synthesis of the Research* (Englewood Cliffs: Prentice Hall, 1979).

8   Lawrence G. Shattuck, "Communicating Intent and Imparting Presence," *Military Review* (March-April, 2000), 66-72.

9   Ibid., 69.

10   Ibid., 71-72.

11   Pigeau and McCann define intent as "an aim or purpose along with all of its associated connotations." They further state that intent should be considered

to comprise both explicit and implicit elements. Explicit intent may be expressed verbally or in written orders. They state, "Implicit intent refers to all of the connotations latent within a specific (that is, explicit) aim. An individual's implicit intent is a combination of habits, experiences, beliefs, and values that reflect personal, military, cultural, and national expectations. Implicit intent … includes deep beliefs based on religion, morals, and values that are to a large extent unconscious and pervasive."

12 Geoffrey Hone, Ian Whitworth and Andy Farmilo, "Assessing the Transmission of Command Intent," Paper presented at the *12ᵗʰ International Command and Control Research and Technology Symposium – Adapting C2 to the 21ˢᵗ Century*, Newport, RI, 2007.

13 It should be noted that this is an interpretation of the method used in the study. In his paper, Murphy states, "The subordinate staff and commanders were asked to consider their commander's intent, and in this light, independently rank the given reaction options in terms of most to least likely to occur." See Peter Murphy, "Forays into Command Intent: Assessing the Components of Intent Statements and Developing a Methodology for Measuring Shared Intent," DSTO-TN-0471 (2002), 5. It is assumed here that participants were really being asked to order response options based on the extent to which they are appropriate to commander's intent.

14 Andrew Leggatt, "Objectively Measuring the Promulgation of Commander's Intent in a Coalition Effects Based Planning Experiment (MNE3)," Paper presented at the *9ᵗʰ International Command and Control Research and Technology Symposium – The Power of Information Age Technologies*, Copenhagen, Denmark, 2004.

15 The presentation associated with this paper indicates that 24 probes were presented over four days, which seems to imply that 60 probe statements were available to the two-star commander. However, it is not clear whether there was any repetition of probe statements. Of particular interest, also, is the way in which the probe statements were developed. It was noted that the statements were designed to reflect the commander's intent and provide a blend of implicit and explicit issues. It was further stressed that the probes did not represent, in verbatim, the published guidance. It is stated that an equal number of true and false statements were developed. However, it is not clear what the balance of true and false was in the statements that were finally presented. It is noted that the commander chose probes daily that he thought most accurately reflected his intent. These always included some true and some false statements but not necessarily in equal number.

16   An inability to understand the intent statement would presumably be more relevant to operational effectiveness than problems understanding the probes.

17   Klein found only five of 35 U.S. Army CI statements to contain "anti-goals." See Gary Klein, "Characteristics of Commander's Intent Statements," Paper presented at the *Symposium on Command and Control Research*, Washington, D.C., 1993. Murphy's survey of Australian Army officers found anti-goals to be rated lowest in importance of eight features of a generic intent statement. See Murphy, "Forays into Command Intent." In a survey of 103 UK military personnel, Molloy and her colleagues asked respondents to indicate what elements they believe a CI statement should include, but no category equivalent to anti-goals was generated. See Jules Molloy, Carol Blendell, Raph Pascual and Al Campbell, "Understanding and Supporting the Effective Formulation, Dissemination and Interpretation of Commander's Intent: Final Technical Working Paper," QINETIQ/KI/CHS/TWP030136/1.0 (2003).

18   Jeffrey Thomas, Linda Pierce, Melissa Dixon and Gwenda Fong, "Interpreting Commander's Intent: Do We Really Know What We Know and What We Don't Know?" Paper presented at the *12th International Command and Control Research and Technology Symposium – Adapting C2 to the 21st Century*, Newport, RI, 2007.

19   Regrettably, owing to constraints of space, it is not feasible to examine this issue further in this chapter. Without doubt, the relationship between the various aspects of intent and situation awareness should be the subject of further research.

20   Thomas et al., "Interpreting Commander's Intent," 14.

21   Philip Farrell, "Measuring Common Intent During Effects Based Planning," Paper presented at the *Command and Control Research and Technology Symposium – The Power of Information Age Concepts and Technologies*, San Diego, CA, 15-17 June 2004.

22   Ibid., 1. Although Leggatt chose to use the term "commander's intent" in his study, both he and Farrell appear to be interested in measuring the same construct. Leggatt does not discount the importance of the implicit aspects of intent, and, as described above, made efforts to ensure that the probe statements used in the study included implicit intent. Leggatt's preference for the term "commander's intent" may be driven by a desire to use terms already familiar and meaningful to the military audience.

23   There appear to be some discrepancies between the Farrell and Leggatt papers concerning the details of the experimental method and procedure. Farrell states that only participants in the CTFHQ answered the 24 probe statements, which according to his paper, implies 64 persons. Leggatt states that 105 participants completed all four sets of commander's intent probes. Farrell notes that the probes addressed explicit intent only, while Leggatt stresses that the probes were a mixture of implicit and explicit. These differences are most likely a result of different data sets being used for analysis in the British and Canadian studies.

24   This indicates that their performance was better than we would expect it to be if they had simply been guessing.

25   Philip Farrell, Dave Allen, Paul Burrows, Paul Comeau, Steven Hughes, John Kachuik, Paul Labbe and Fred Lichacz, "Multi-National Experiment 4 on Effects-Based Approach to Operations – CFEC Analysis Report," DRDC-Ottawa TR 2006-230. Intent analyses were also conducted by the UK team involved in MNE4 using Leggatt's technique as described above. Regrettably, at the time of writing, the reports of the UK analyses were not yet available to the author.

26   Philip Farrell, "Calculating Effectiveness Using Bi-polar Scales and Vector Algebra," DRDC-Toronto TR 2005-148 (June 2005).

27   Molloy et al., "Final Technical Working Paper."

28   The important question of whether CI defines a specific course of action or less tightly defined boundary conditions within which subordinates are free to develop their own solutions is beyond the scope of the current chapter and will be the focus of future research.

CHAPTER 6

Designing Net-Centric Interfaces to Capture Commander's Intent * ◆

Brian P. Donnelly and Scott M. Galster

AIR FORCE RESEARCH LABORATORY,
WRIGHT-PATTERSON AIR FORCE BASE,
OHIO, USA

INTRODUCTION

> *Command includes both the authority and responsibility for effectively using available resources to accomplish assigned missions. Command at all levels is the art of motivating and directing people and organizations into action to accomplish missions. The art of command lies in conscious and skillful exercise of command authority through visualization, decision making, and leadership.*[1]

Underwriting every military operation, no matter the magnitude, is Commander's Intent: the vision and desired end-state of the mission. Under normal operating conditions, that intent is translated into actionable objectives that each participating unit uses to build its part of what culminates as a synchronized operation. As things change when first contact with the enemy is made, the intent may

---

* For clarity, in this paper the term "Commander's Intent" is used as both a proper noun (and is therefore capitalized) and noun (no capitalization).

◆ Cleared for Public Release by AFRL/WS Public Affairs. Disposition Date: 11/07/2007. Document Number: WPAFB 07-0367.

or may not evolve to meet new operational demands. How quickly required changes are recognized and accommodated translates into how well the operation as a whole acts as a single entity, and in doing so, how well it meets the commander's intent both efficiently and effectively.

The face of warfare has changed significantly since the latter half of the 20th century. With the release of the Soviet Bloc from communism, the explosive growth of the Internet and the increased instability in the Middle East, the challenges for the U.S. military have shifted from predominantly traditional warfare between nations (typified by the Cold War standoff between the two superpowers), towards a continuum of irregular, catastrophic and disruptive challenges. Defending against non-state actors has caused senior civilian and military leaders to re-evaluate traditional thinking. There is now a concerted effort to balance preserving the capability to defend against a near peer with new capabilities to "find, fix and finish" needles in haystacks (i.e., insurgents blending into populations).

While information technology (IT) and the Internet are opening the doors to information sharing on an unprecedented scale, it has been both a blessing and a curse for civil and military organizations as they struggle to take advantage of network-centric operations and information sharing. For example, network-centric operations enable forces to be linked as never before, but protecting networks and the information that they contain from corruption or manipulation is a growing challenge. The experience of 9/11 served as a catalyst for seamless intelligence sharing in the hunt for the next catastrophic insurgent cell. Hurricane Katrina similarly triggered a call for seamless emergency response to a catastrophe of a different kind on an even larger scale. Faster, scalable response, higher fidelity intelligence, tighter synchronization of efforts, more efficient use of resources – all are requirements for, as well as intended consequences of, network-centric operations in general and the Global War on Terror in particular.

Fifty years ago, limitations on the speed of communications meant that it took days or weeks to amass enough information for decision-making at the operational level. With the advent of the Information Age and the promise of network-centric warfare (NCW), however, decision cycles have been compressed to minutes for some time-sensitive actions. Asymmetric threats, potentially a single person employing a weapon of mass destruction (WMD), are driving the need for even faster decisions: "finding to finishing" in seconds, potentially. This operational tempo strains the command and control elements of the force and can severely stress commanders even when operating under a "centralized control, decentralized execution" philosophy. The NCW Maturity Model postulates that increasing interoperability, not only in the information domain but also in the cognitive and social domains, will yield the potential for shared situation awareness (SA) and self-synchronization, the combination of which NCW advocates have labeled "Power to the Edge."[2]

It is necessary, but not sufficient however, that key information be available throughout the network. On 9/11, information was available that might have limited the damage of the terrorist teams that boarded the flights that morning. Granted, that information was fragmented across several agencies, but even if all the intelligence on the conspirators had been in a single database, there was still "something" missing. That "something" was shared logic: logic that would have produced flags at airport check-in counters for the flights that those individuals identified as potential terrorists intended to board; logic that would have looked for combinations of names on manifests; logic that would have tracked one-way ticket purchases in combination with specific names; logic that may have caused air marshals to fly on specific flights; logic that would have requested warrants for arrests in parallel with the search for suspected individuals; logic that may have flagged and tracked airliners deviating from flight plans (and not following proper Interrogation Friend or Foe (IFF) transponder procedures for civilian air traffic); logic that would have relayed aircraft position and vector information automatically to AWACS (Airborne Warning and Control System) or fighter aircraft scrambled to intercept them. The system, however, would still be incomplete without the rule-sets to enable the system to both bring that information to the attention of operators who might act upon it and then maintain both tracking and identification (ID) continuity until the targets had been neutralized. Even if all the logic on the machine side of the interface is in place, humans need to recognize critical information, possibly simultaneously in multiple locations, to take any of a number of the steps needed to stop a catastrophic sequence of events from reaching its conclusion. While no one person can do it all, the team of people whose complementary roles embody the "mission" must recognize the actionable information and then act as one during a crisis. "Acting as one" is the purpose of Commander's Intent: giving the team the vision of the end-state so they can continue to act as one through contingencies caused by both coincidental events (i.e., the "fog and friction of war"), as well as deliberate acts of the enemy.

Decision-making relies on information, and while some logic can be encoded and processed in microseconds by machines, most decisions still require an operator "in the loop." Designing user interfaces to support achieving Commander's Intent requires looking at information handling from both sides of the interface and aligning the logic to support decisions made on both time scales. Interface concepts that focus on capturing and preserving Commander's Intent can provide an integrating function for both operators' shared understanding of the situation and the apportionment of resources across the network supporting the operation. By grounding both the logic employed in the networked resource management and the method of visualizing the shared "picture" on Commander's Intent, synergies anticipated from network-centric operations may be reasonably achieved.

IT can be thought of as tools that extend human capability in data handling and information manipulation. The logic that might coordinate those data handling and information manipulation actions across a network of systems can similarly be thought of as an extension of a social network – interoperability in the social domain – working at light speed. In a battlefield scenario, that logic might be responsible for aligning how resources are expended: where sensors are scanning for critical information on the enemy; where supplies are positioned for replacing consumable items (i.e., food, fuel, ordnance, etc.); and communicating the "plan" to the participating units so that they know when and where to be vigilant or to take a rest. That logic is incomplete without a means to represent it in a shared "picture" that embodies a common understanding of the Joint Force Commander's (JFC) strategy and intent – interoperability in the cognitive domain. The shared picture provides the means to analyze where we have been, see where we are, and plan where we intend to go simultaneously, and also to look at resources from tactical to operational to strategic perspectives.

*"The focus of command and control is the **commander**."*[3]

For operators and their IT, Commander's Intent, as translated into plans for execution, needs to guide how resources are consumed and how information is produced. A necessary ingredient to achieving distributed, synchronized net-centric operations is a human-IT partnership such as has never before been created. Human training and experience with doctrine, combined with computational capacities to evaluate thousands of parameters simultaneously using embedded logic, both need to work in unison to successfully accomplish the mission and achieve the end-state vision. What follows in this chapter is a limited, initial description of some of the user interface concepts that, when mature, will create this partnership of human and machine. Included is both a notional description of a common visualization framework for command and control (C2) operators (the common "picture") and an hypothetical prioritization taxonomy for managing resources (in this case, sensor management, the means of maintaining that "picture"). By taking a balanced approach to developing both sides of the human-machine interface, it is possible to capture the JFC's intent in how the battlespace is sensed and how it is portrayed "to the edge."

IMPROVING THE HUMAN SIDE OF THE INTERFACE

> *Battlefield visualization is the process whereby the commander develops a clear understanding of his current state with relation to the enemy and environment, envisions a desired end-state, and then visualizes the sequence of activities that will move his force from its current state to the end-state. In short, it provides the key to where and how the commander can best lead and motivate soldiers, and see the battlefield, his own forces, the enemy, and the end-state. It is critical to mission accomplishment that commanders have the ability to visualize the battlefield. Therefore, in his intent statement, the commander must clearly articulate his battlefield visualization to his subordinates and staff to ensure the optimum development and execution of his concept of operations.*[4]

In essence, what is needed is a means of sharing SA within the context of the commander's intent and strategy, commonly and ubiquitously, in order to promote decision-making that can facilitate mission success. A common definition of SA is "the perception of the elements in the environment within a volume of time and space, the comprehension of their meaning and the projection of their status in the near future."[5] The link between time and space, and the ability to project forward, are critical elements of a redesigned interface. The necessary ingredients for the collection of C2 operators to act as one arguably include: common direction (Commander's Intent and subsequent detailed mission tasking); sufficient mission training and experience; a common method of sampling elements of the environment and communicating (i.e., a user interface); and tools for filtering information to reach decisions quickly and efficiently. While the concept of capturing Commander's Intent throughout the C2 network of systems as part of doctrine is not new,[6] capturing it on both sides of the user interface is a novel approach and will require a robust research effort to demonstrate and document best practices.

To date, the best doctrinal definition of Commander's Intent is:

> [Commander's Intent] is a concise expression of the purpose of the operation and must be understood two echelons below the issuing commander. It must clearly state the purpose of the mission. It is the single unifying focus for all subordinate elements. It is not a summary of the concept of the operation. Its purpose is to focus subordinates on the desired end-state. Its utility is to focus subordinates on what has to be accomplished in order to achieve success, even when the plan and concept of operations no longer apply, and to discipline their efforts toward that end.[7]

That concise expression is translated into strategic objectives, which begin to define not only planned actions, but also their subsequent sequencing. Strategic objectives are further decomposed into operational and tactical objectives. Planning staffs at all levels examine the options available to achieve mission success and select plans that maximize expected outcomes while minimizing known risks. The result? The choreography of units' actions over time (kinetic, in geospace, and non-kinetic, in cyberspace) to achieve objectives, the sum of which should be the realization of Commander's Intent.

One fundamental doctrinal precept is that if subordinates understand the commander's intent, they can synchronize their actions with the overarching plan to reach the successful end-state. The difficulty, documented during and after every conflict, is that plans seldom survive first contact with a thinking enemy and the "fog of war" inhibits readily changing choreography once it has begun.[8] To realize coordination and coherency, significant research needs to hone in on how to better capture Commander's Intent on both sides of the human-machine interface for C2 systems. Commander's Intent encompasses both space and time – it is the vision of where the commander wants to be in the future – and transcends the spectrum of planning and execution from strategic to tactical. Similarly, methods of improving the user interface that also transcend strategic to tactical operators' information needs, while maintaining the coupling of space and time, need to be developed. The discussion that follows presents notional concepts of how that might be implemented.

As highlighted in the 2005 *National Defense Strategy* and again in the 2006 *Quadrennial Defense Review Report,* the challenges the U.S. and other allied militaries will face in the immediate future are more asymmetric than traditional, with non-state actors choosing irregular, catastrophic and disruptive methods over direct military attacks. While each of these challenges requires a somewhat unique approach in response, there is more commonality than difference and all military actions require a commander's authorization and some amount of planning.

Before any operation begins, intelligence is collected and made available for planning. The quantity and quality of that intelligence typically depends on the geo-political area in question and its strategic value to the interests of the nation. Intelligence data is useful only insofar as there is a meaningful context available for its interpretation. If the interpretation suggests a requirement for military action, then detailed planning (typically based on standing plans, but not necessarily) begins to refine the options available for the Commander-in-Chief. Figure 6-1 graphically portrays how Commander's Intent flows through the levels of war (in this case, to a Combined Air & Space Operations Center (CAOC)). From that intent, strategic planners develop objectives from which operational and tactical planners build the details of a campaign.

Once an operation is approved and in its execution phase, the analysis, execution and planning functions all simultaneously support the commander's intent. There are many paths of varying risk that can lead to mission success and each requires a different combination of resources. Communicating the selected path and managing resources is typically done at the operational level, through an operations centre. For traditional warfare involving air assets, this is one of the roles of the CAOC via the Air Tasking Order process. No matter how short the duration of an operation, analysis, execution and planning functions all must simultaneously support the commander. While the Intelligence, Surveillance and Reconnaissance (ISR) assets provide the commander's eyes, ears and analysis, the C2 systems manage the execution of the approved plan (i.e., the resource management, which includes the ISR assets that establish and maintain the "picture"), make changes to handle contingencies, and monitor and control the weapons systems and supporting resources to achieve the commander's intent.

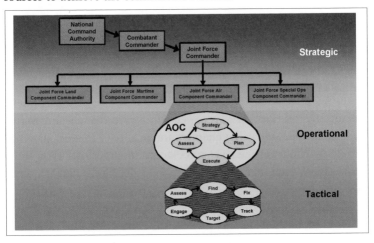

Figure 6-1: Levels of War: The Flow of Commander's Intent. (Note: AOC = Air and Space Operations Center)

Since the battle is conducted in space and time, it makes sense to monitor and manage it within the framework of its spatial and temporal dimensions. The objective of battle management is the maintenance of a level of SA at which operators are able to accurately forecast future situation events and dynamics (e.g., Level 3 SA)[9] and make decisions that maintain the initiative. Yet most battle management systems provide only a two-dimensional snapshot in time updated at discrete intervals (associated with the availability of sensor data). Such displays are deficient in at least two respects. First, they portray only latitude and longitude. This means that an aircraft's altitude and the terrain elevation data need to be coded using an alternative, arguably less intuitive, scheme. Second, time is

113

conveyed only by the change of position of entities on the display. It is not represented as a continuous dimension. One can neither look forward (as represented by the plan) nor backward (as represented by archived data). An operator recognizes what has changed only by means of his or her memory or by displaying track histories. This places an inordinate burden on the C2 operators to collectively recognize trends and make a coordinated response without tools available that directly help to do that work.

"Effective C2 demands that commanders and staffs collaborate in forming and articulating commander's intent and determining the mission, operational objectives, desired effects, and tasks."[10]

Many C2 and intelligence operators make use of a three-dimensional (3-D) situation display to perform their tasks. These exist in a host of government-owned and commercial-off-the-shelf (COTS) varieties. The utility of 3-D representations remains, however, an open question, as human factors researchers have failed to demonstrate consistently their superiority for tasks relevant to battle management.[11] It is likely that 3-D representations are good for some tasks or sub-tasks, are poor for others, and that there are performance trade-offs between the two. To date, there has been no comprehensive program of research to explore this space parametrically.

Even less experimental work has looked at representing the temporal dimension in battle management. Although some display designers have provided a temporal display in the form of a dynamic Gantt chart,[12] this has typically been an alternative view rather than an integrated or linked component of the geo-spatial display and has typically been used for planning rather than execution. It is proposed that a four-dimensional (4-D) visual display linking the three spatial dimensions with time will enhance operator SA and promote improved planning, execution and analysis.

The 4-D display proposed herein might look something like a book, with the temporal and geo-spatial components residing on opposite pages. Figure 6-2 offers a description of the content of the temporal display. Note that where update rates are mentioned, the implication is that there is a variable quality of service (latency and precedence) commensurate with the level of information accuracy required by the operators working within that segment of the temporal space.[13] So, for example, where critical information relating to a target's position is being relayed for a fire control solution, the quality of information required (i.e., positional accuracy) is very high. This, in turn, requires sensors to revisit targets at a frequency that will produce and sustain the required accuracy until the mission is complete. From this example, it should be obvious that a target with the ability to rapidly change its position or identification characteristics would place a heavy burden on sensor resources. Integrating active radar sensor technology into air-to-air missiles over the past several decades was a direct consequence of trying to relieve this burden at the very tactical level.

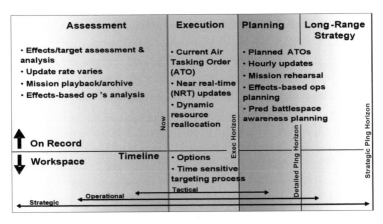

Figure 6-2: Components of the Temporal Display (within the 4-D construct).

The proposed display would be divided horizontally by a timeline, and vertically by significant "times," including time "Now," the current execution horizon, the detailed planning horizon, and the strategic planning horizon. Each area is delineated by color to highlight the primary focus and the principal group of operators (e.g., analysts, warfighters in execution, and planners) using data/information within each temporal zone. Above the timeline (right to left) would be both the plan of record, changes to it made within the execution window including options exercised, and the archive of what was recorded as "truth." Below the timeline (right to left) would be options being considered but not on record, real-time options held during execution but not taken, and an archived history of both the plan before execution and the options held for execution but not taken.

Attributes of the temporal display would include scalability (zoom-in to a minute-scale or zoom-out to a months-scale), mission-relevant information update rates (as discussed earlier, near real-time during execution, as-needed for analysis and planning), and methods for filtering the information presented relative to the role of the operator in the C2 network (by kinetic or non-kinetic missions, by targets, by objectives, etc.). Each of these attributes would contribute to linking tactical to strategic operators, conducting assessment, planning or execution roles. While each operator will tend to use information filtered, scaled and updated to his/her mission need, the 4-D display itself would be a common framework enabling shared SA across the entire C2 community. The temporal display would complement the geo-spatial display and would conceivably be a permanent "left-hand" display to match the geo-spatial on the right. Taken together, this conceptual 4-D display could be the common picture capturing the confluence of analysis, planning and execution information. It would not replace tools and applications needed for conducting different roles in battle management; it would instead represent the aggregate of contributions to the "true" picture (as close to truth as the human-machine partnership could produce, portray and archive).

The temporal display could be linked to the geo-spatial display, so that as an operator selects items on the temporal side, they are simultaneously highlighted on the geo-spatial side (the linkage could also be broken in order to keep one side as a reference while searching for information on the other). Selecting an asset or target on the geo-spatial display would dynamically point to information, for example, relevant to that asset's mission or the target's status, with results and analysis temporally linked for ease of reference. By selecting a block of time in the future or past, operators could visually rehearse a mission or see it played back as it was flown, filtering the plan or the archive as needed for items of interest. One important benefit in having a temporal display is the ability of an operator to examine where reality caused assets to deviate from the plan in time. Because most plans incorporate tight coupling between assets temporally, deviations from the plan that might have cascading effects can potentially be identified more readily and handled efficiently. For example, if a KC-135 scheduled to conduct air refuelling at one altitude requested and was approved a change in anchor altitude due to weather conditions, highlighting the change on the temporal display might be more readily seen and coordinated with other assets impacted by the change. In a related way, showing the planned versus actual location on the spatial display would similarly enable coordination with all involved.

The selling point of the temporal display is that it represents more than just a snapshot in time and therefore allows operators to achieve greater levels of SA,[14] which has been raised as a limitation of traditional geo-spatial displays.[15] On the other hand, it is difficult to "picture" temporal data outside of a geo-spatial context, so the two are really complementary. Patterns may be discovered through examination of the temporal display that might go unnoticed monitoring only the geo-spatial picture.

Adding the temporal dimension itself is not the novelty. Most so-called 4-D displays are simply geo-spatial displays with a VCR-like playback capability, which falls far short of the user interface required to capture Commander's Intent. The primary benefit of portraying the battlespace in four dimensions is that the real world is a four-dimensional space. We live, think and fight in four dimensions, and so it seems intuitively reasonable that we should monitor, assess, plan and execute in four dimensions as well. As time can be scaled to minutes or months, information relevant to tactical through strategic interests can be portrayed, thus transcending the levels of command using the same display framework. Among the most powerful features of this 4-D display concept is its ability to capture Commander's Intent such that every operator, at every level of the operation, can trace his or her role to the JFC's priorities. The following sequence of figures and supporting text illustrate this concept.

Figure 6-3 shows a speculative temporal view of the JFC's strategic objectives (note that the scale is strategic: highest objectives on a timescale of months). The elevator bar to the right indicates the resolution/timescale, while the tabs represent potential aggregates of information to be viewed at the strategic level, such as the Commander's Intent message, the derived strategic objectives (as selected here), and the corresponding effects desired/anticipated.

In this display, the operator is able to move the cursor over one of the objectives and see a pop-up text box describing the objective in detail, or right-click on it to obtain additional detail or take other actions relating to that specific objective. At this resolution, strategic planners and assessors could compare progress against metrics at the strategic level and re-plan at the campaign level as required. Tactical operators may not ever need to spend time at this temporal resolution, but they would be afforded the opportunity to trace their mission(s) to the overarching JFC's intent.

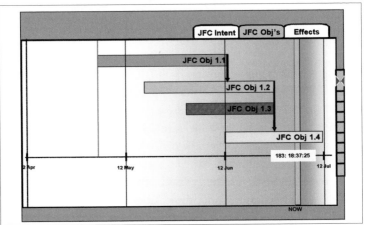

Figure 6-3: Strategic Objectives as Portrayed on a Notional Temporal Display.

Continuing the example, if the operator selects JFC Objective 1.4, the timescale automatically expands to display the operational objectives supporting that strategic objective. See Figure 6-4. Again, only a subset of staff officers and commanders will spend time working with information at this level as it relates to apportionment of resources at the operational level. What is critical is the traceability to Commander's Intent and the linkage to tactical objectives and effects. This might be the level at which Commander's Critical Information Requirements (CCIRs) are viewed as well. Although not depicted here, they are critical to assessing the operational environment and they identify decision points in the course of the campaign.[16] Again, the tabs at the top of the display represent the ability to directly visit a page that might present the JFC's intent in text form, or an alternate method of viewing the effects that, in this case, would correspond to JFC Objective 1.4.

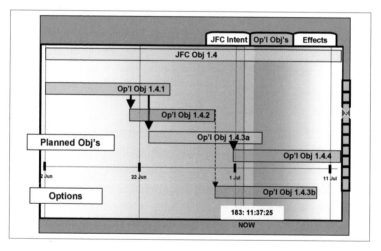

Figure 6-4: Operational Objectives Supporting JFC Objective 1.4.

In Figure 6-5, the linkage between operational level and tactical levels is highlighted. Tactical objectives might take days or possibly weeks to accomplish and would link directly with packages of resources apportioned to create tactical effects. When considered in the aggregate, tactical effects should cause operational effects.

Assessing intended versus unintended effects is a critical function at the operational level of C2 and would be part of the parametric analysis of tactical and operational objective completion and their corresponding effects.

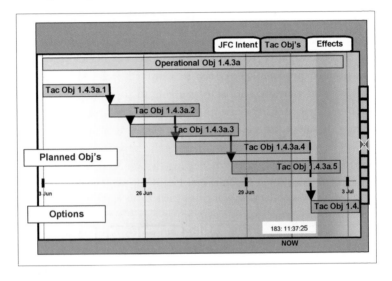

Figure 6-5: Tactical Objectives Supporting Operational Objective 1.4.3a.

At the next level of resolution, kinetic and non-kinetic "packages" of resources will be planned and apportioned to create tactical effects. A tactical operator might use the display to "drill down" to the mission level to monitor only the aircraft in one of the packages supporting a tactical objective that in turn supports one of the operational objectives shown in Figure 6-6. At this tactical resolution, mission details relevant to the tactical operator could be selected for display as well. In this example, the missions that refuelled while airborne can be identified by the bar within the bar of their mission timeline (here depicted in yellow in Figure 6-7).

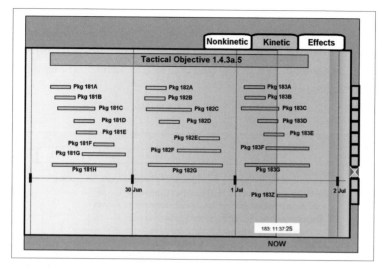

Figure 6-6: Packages Corresponding to a Tactical Objective.

At this resolution, the scale has automatically expanded to minutes/ hours. As this package has already flown, the background is a fading color to identify time as post-"Now" (here pictured in fading blue to white, with white being the more distant past). Time "Now" is still displayed in a box at the corner of the display, but the line depicting "Now" is off this screen. Information such as mission results could be accessed by selecting an individual mission (rolling cursor over and pausing, or right-clicking and selecting from a list of options, notionally). If the missions were currently airborne, selecting one or multiple missions in time would also highlight them on the geospatial display for ease of reference.

It is especially important to emphasize that this notional 4-D display, with tactical- to strategic-scalable resolution, enables operators to see the linkage between Commander's Intent and individual missions and portrays information such that it is relevant to all those who monitor, assess, plan and execute (MAPE) missions in the battlespace. It does not replace the tools that individuals use to perform their mission. Instead, it serves as the common display that promotes a shared understanding of the battlespace in space and time. It is the aggregation of many operators' inputs through a variety of applications that populate databases from which the display pulls its content. While it is conceivable that alerts might be input directly onto the global 4-D display, most, if not all, data displayed would be from a central repository database.

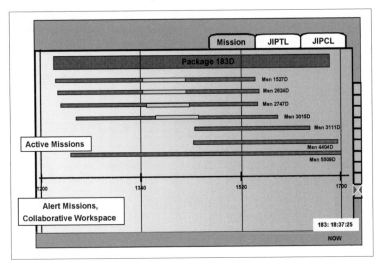

Figure 6-7: Missions within Package 183-D (timescale in minutes).

It is also important to point out that there are examples of temporal displays with some of the attributes outlined above already developed. One example is the display recently demonstrated at Air Mobility Command's (AMC's) Tanker Airlift Control Center (TACC) under the Work-centered Interface Distributed Environment (WIDE) advanced technology demonstration (ATD) program. The WIDE temporal display provides AMC operators global visibility into their airlift fleet, allowing them to quickly recognize the impacts of changes during mission execution.[17] Figures 6-8 and 6-9 are examples from WIDE of what the temporal view at a tactical resolution of the notional 4-D display might look like.

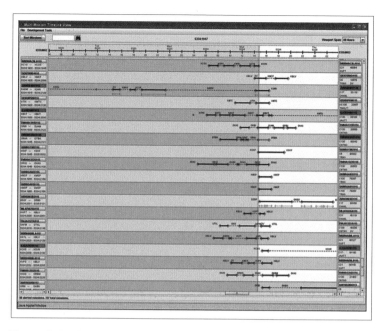

Figure 6-8: Multi-Mission View, WIDE ATD.

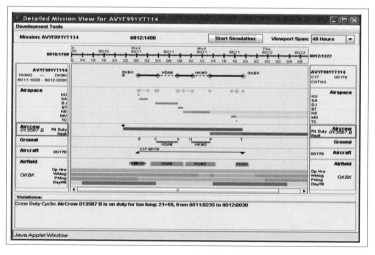

Figure 6-9: Single-Mission View, WIDE ATD.

The WIDE visualization separates itself from other time-oriented displays in that it maps out the operators decision space with views of missions and their resource constraints on a common timescale that is updated with near real-time AMC mission data. Since the visualization depicts their "problem in context," operators are able to rapidly understand the meaning of an alert and "see" the factors affecting mission viability and possible solutions. Another significant capability is the ability to perform "what-if" simulations to gain future SA of the repercussions of any changes to the mission itinerary. This unique capability allows the operator to react to mission problems with actionable information in a timely manner.

The WIDE temporal display was recently evaluated in an operational scenario using simulated data with a variety of TACC execution personnel. Performance in realistic work scenarios using the timeline concept and AMC's existing system was compared. With the timeline, operators were significantly faster at re-planning missions with fewer errors and a decrease in cognitive workload. They also attained greater SA on the repercussions of mission changes.[18]

Finally, it must be noted that the examples depicted in the preceding paragraphs describe display *concepts*, not specific displays (except in the case of WIDE). Moreover, the purported benefits of these display concepts are hypothetical. In order to properly assess the utility of 4-D displays like the one proposed, a program of research designed to evaluate the performance of operators using such displays in laboratory and operational conditions is warranted. Laboratory and field investigations could be used to assess the effects of the displays on SA, workload and task performance. Should these prove fruitful, the display might be tested in an operational exercise to determine its effect on mission outcomes.

IMPROVING THE MACHINE SIDE OF THE INTERFACE

> *Every commander must make decisions concerning the allocation, commitment, and engagement of troops and resources. In turn, the commander must give his staff the authority to make routine decisions, within the constraints of the commander's intent, while conducting operations. The C2 system is the tool by which the commander quickly distributes his decisions to his subordinate commanders.*[19]

To capture Commander's Intent in C2 interfaces, a balanced approach that works both sides of the human-machine boundary is required. There was a time when Artificial Intelligence and "thinking machines" were hot topics for military applications. While the hype has waned somewhat, the necessity for a human-machine partnership has increased with the advent of NCW. There are specific steps that can be taken to ease the burden of sifting through the new mountains of information available as a result of network-centric operations. Without proper throttling of information, information pipes either indiscriminately flood operators with both useful and irrelevant information or they become bottlenecks that degrade network performance. Just as operators are constantly sifting through data and information to gather what they need to make decisions, so too should the network-centric systems supporting them. Battle management is a combination of risk management and resource management applied to conflict. As there are never enough resources to reduce risk to zero, the JFC sets priorities, and from his priorities are derived classes of priorities for managing ISR resources, re-supply resources, etc., and for finding, fixing, tracking, targeting, engaging and assessing (F2T2EA) targets.

Translating a commander's priorities into logic that a network of systems can use to help human operators manage a battle should not be difficult; having a coalition of international partners agree to the prioritization taxonomy and then integrate that logic into their systems such that they operate in concert on a network *will be.* Without near-universal agreement on the taxonomy, networked systems will "fight" over resources and priority inversions will plague the network (i.e., important information will suffer or be suppressed, while less important information is shared). Many resources are "owned" or controlled by one community within the JFC's force (e.g., tanker assets are controlled by a commander subordinate to the Joint Force Air Component Commander (JFACC) or by the JFACC himself) and therefore are more easily managed. Targets (e.g., combatant enemy forces), on the other hand, are closer to "everyone's business" and require a multitude of unit coordination in the F2T2EA process. To capture Commander's Intent on the machine-side of the user interface, a common prioritization taxonomy needs to be agreed upon and the logic integrated into C2 systems. Before going through a notional taxonomy and an example of its use, it is important to first briefly discuss how priorities are derived.

Some amount of intelligence precedes every situation where forces are mobilized and employed. When an area of geo-political interest becomes "hot," intelligence efforts increase. The goal is to identify priority elements in the potential battlespace (people, facilities, weapons, etc.) and then track changes for analysis and decision-making. While intelligence can never provide a "truth" picture (everything perfectly identified and tracked), such an image is, nevertheless, the goal for at least those elements relevant to the situation. The more a JFC knows going into a conflict and throughout the campaign, the better his or her ability to employ the force and make decisions. Given that resources are limited, the determination of priorities and the expenditure of ISR resources is a matter of risk management. It may be impossible to track every pedestrian in a city for even a few seconds, but it is critical to find, fix, track, target and engage the terrorist disguised as a pedestrian who happens to be attempting to employ a weapon on a large civilian population.

At this point, it is necessary to point out that the current targeting process assigns all targets a priority and the ISR network of systems collects information according to the CCIRs that include priority intelligence requirements on the enemy as well as friendly force information requirements.[20] What is proposed below, however, builds on that priority schema and is specifically designed to aid the IT supporting the Commander's Intent. The description and taxonomy described below are conceptual and not part of current doctrine.

Priority, as it is used here, is a function of an entity's 1) identification (in the case of an enemy, the ID obtained by the Combat ID (CID) process), 2) location, 3) inherent capability (including changes in capability, e.g., battle damage assessment), and 4) engagement status. It is a dynamic measure of an object's relevance to the battlespace, whether that be for targeting, collecting intelligence information, monitoring or some other function. In the case of a terrorist looking to employ a WMD, ID and location relevance should be clear. The terrorist's location with respect to a population centre will establish how much time a commander has to decide and act. Inherent capability includes both the capability of the weapon and the capability of the transporting system (in this case, the terrorist himself, and whether he is healthy, wounded, etc.). Engagement status includes whether the terrorist is being prosecuted as a target already and the need to support the friendly forces conducting the mission. One can imagine that a healthy terrorist with an armed WMD within a population center would have a high, if not *the* highest, priority among the target list. The priority would cause the sensor network to cross-cue continuously so that the quality of information on the target remained very high. Losing such a target in a crowd would be unthinkable, and potentially devastating, and relaying accurate information on target location and ID would be critical to engaging forces.

Note that the taxonomy described below in Figure 6-10 is purely hypothetical. Reaching agreement on a common taxonomy for network automation among a coalition of nations will require intense involvement of, and development with, the operational communities involved. For this taxonomy, a 0-1000 scale was chosen because it allows enough flexibility to capture the different sub-elements of prioritization. It is important to note that, given only 1000 discrete priorities, there will be many tracked entities with the same priority.

In an area of interest (AOI) of, say, a city block in Manhattan where the NCW system is trying to track a single person of interest, one can imagine there being thousands of 001-priority civilians walking through the streets or riding elevators in buildings. When the person of interest is positively identified, however, his priority would automatically rise to 799 (if the system is automatically performing the ID) or rise to 999 if an operator is manually setting the ID. This distinction between an automatic and a manual priority value points out a key feature that will need to be incorporated into the logic of the automation: the distinction between Rules of Identification (ROI) and Rules of Engagement (ROE).

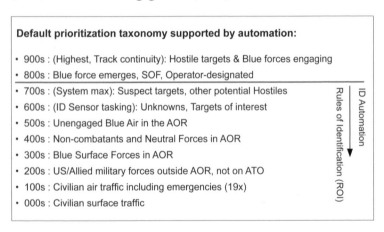

Default prioritization taxonomy supported by automation:

- 900s : (Highest, Track continuity): Hostile targets & Blue forces engaging
- 800s : Blue force emerges, SOF, Operator-designated
- 700s : (System max): Suspect targets, other potential Hostiles
- 600s : (ID Sensor tasking): Unknowns, Targets of interest
- 500s : Unengaged Blue Air in the AOR
- 400s : Non-combatants and Neutral Forces in AOR
- 300s : Blue Surface Forces in AOR
- 200s : US/Allied military forces outside AOR, not on ATO
- 100s : Civilian air traffic including emergencies (19x)
- 000s : Civilian surface traffic

Rules of Identification (ROI) | ID Automation

Figure 6-10: Notional Prioritization Taxonomy for C2 and Automation.

ROI is best described as the logic by which an entity is identified. Automating ROI requires that specific rules or logic be encoded for continual, dynamic evaluation on the machine side of the interface, allowing operators to override that ID as they find necessary. As sensor data is accumulated and correlated to any particular entity, it is important that that entity not experience an ambiguity, or the process starts again. Ambiguities occur when two or more entities become indistinguishable by proximity (their locations are within a single resolution cell of the sensor network) or when tracking continuity is lost (the object cannot be tracked by the sensor network for a threshold amount of time). It should be obvious that the best sensors, and networks of sensors, are those that can resolve objects' IDs and/or locations quickly and maintain that resolution under a variety of challenging conditions. While more resource intense, positive ID is a prerequisite for any weapons employment.

ROE, on the other hand, involves human reasoning that is not easily captured in machine logic (e.g., legal limits that may apply to some forces and not others, or combinations of rules, some of which may change from day to day). Unlike ROI, with the focus more to establish ID, ROE seeks to determine intent (friendly or hostile) and can lead to weapons employment. Because weapons should never be employed without a human operator making the decision, for both moral and legal reasons, the prioritization taxonomy below limits labeling targets to "Friend," "Neutral," "Unknown" or "Suspect" (i.e., dynamic priorities of 799 or less), which is below the threshold for engagement. "Hostile" is reserved for manual input only.

This taxonomy represents an initial concept of how dynamic prioritization might occur across a C2 network for a designated Area of Responsibility (AOR, i.e., the area of operations for a combatant commander), and is based upon the primary author's experience in the air-to-air environment. While the scale was arbitrarily selected, it balances having too many gradations against the need for granularity among many types of tracked entities. The important factor is that it supports automating the network of sensors, communication links, etc., to support the human C2 network. It does this by encoding relative importance on all tracked entities in the battlespace, friendly or otherwise. Again, ID, location, capability and engagement status are all considered in determining priority; priority then determines some amount of resource utilization. For the ISR network, this would equate to maintaining required accuracies to maintain ID and tracking continuity. For the combat air forces, this would equate to accuracies required to support targeting hostiles, providing combat search-and-rescue for downed aircrew, or providing special mission support to other high priority friendly missions.

The finer gradations within the taxonomy are left out for simplicity. Suffice it to say that other elements that would be worth distinguishing within the categories below might include: capability to self-report position (e.g., via tactical data links); ID conflicts where human intelligence may need to override automated data collected; sub-categorization between similar entities (e.g., vehicles that may be operated in more than one configuration); etc.

The following are some key points to be drawn from this taxonomy:

1) The system (or C2 constellation) should be limited in how it automatically updates a priority and that limit is the threshold between ROI and ROE (depicted here by a red line). No weapons should ever be employed based on a system-only ID without an authorized operator making that determination (i.e., applying ROE).

2) New tracks, or "Unknowns," enter the system with a reasonably high priority (600s). This triggers the ISR network to accumulate data and correlate information to assign an ID (e.g., Friend, Neutral, Suspect and Unknown are the automatic ID categories; Hostile designation is reserved for operators with ID authority). It is important to keep the number of Unknowns to a minimum. This class of entities will usually be the primary focus of ISR assets.

3) The 800s equate to a special category of operator-assigned priority for tracks including battle-damaged Blue forces returning to base, special operations forces, or other high priority tracks (e.g., combat search-and-rescue forces) based on their capabilities or cargo.

4) This taxonomy is based on the earlier referenced concept that priority is a function of CID, geographical location, organic capability and engagement status.

5) When a Blue force entity engages an enemy, its priority automatically rises to match that of the target. This ensures that required tracking accuracy and continuity are maintained on both Blue and Red throughout the engagement to ensure mission success and that histories are as accurate as possible in the event that search-and-rescue is required.

6) Finally, higher priority tracks will require more resources to either positively ID them, maintain their tracking continuity, or both. Should the network performance ever degrade, the lowest priority tracks should be affected first, with appropriate alerting.

The following example illustrates how the taxonomy and automation should work within a single system or across the C2 constellation and is based on an air-to-air engagement scenario. Note that some of the dynamic prioritization is automatic, while some is operator-driven. Figure 6-11 outlines the scenario's progression over time. The symbols would be on the geo-spatial display, moving as the entities move in real space. The priorities are attributes of each entity, and that information may or may not be displayed by the operator, but would factor into the network's automation of sensor resources to maintain tracking and CID continuity.

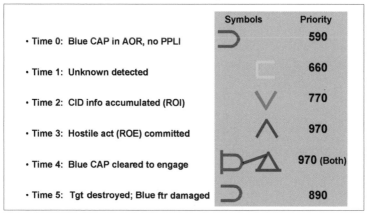

	Symbols	Priority
• Time 0: Blue CAP in AOR, no PPLI		590
• Time 1: Unknown detected		660
• Time 2: CID info accumulated (ROI)		770
• Time 3: Hostile act (ROE) committed		970
• Time 4: Blue CAP cleared to engage		970 (Both)
• Time 5: Tgt destroyed; Blue ftr damaged		890

Figure 6-11: Dynamic Prioritization in an Air-to-Air Scenario.

The scenario unfolds as follows:

1) At Time 0, a Blue force F-15C on a combat air patrol (CAP) mission begins searching the AOR and is not reporting its position via the data-link (i.e., no precise position location information (PPLI)). The Blue force flight has an automatic priority 590, based on CID, location, weapon system capability and engagement status.

2) At some point during the mission, Time 1, an unknown airborne object is detected and automatically given priority 660, triggering the ISR network to rapidly accumulate data to better the ID. The flight on CAP is alerted to the Unknown via tactical data links.

3) When specific information is correlated to the track, Time 2, the system automatically generates a new ID of Suspect based on the ID matrix from the daily instructions. The priority for a Suspect at that location is 770, and the category change focuses the surveillance operators' attention to apply expertise and watch for ROE determinants to be met.

4) At Time 3, the Suspect track commits a hostile act, noted by the surveillance operators, who then recommend to the ID authority that the ID be changed manually to Hostile, raising the priority to 970 (again, based on CID, location, capability, etc.).

5) According to the ROE, this ID change also triggers the Blue force CAP to engage the Hostile, now at Time 4, and the Blue CAP priority moves to 970 as well.

6) Finally, at Time 5, the engagement is over with the target destroyed, but the Blue force fighters have at least one battle-damaged aircraft. They communicate this to the C2

operator who manually sets the track priority to 890 until the aircraft are recovered safely at their base. This higher priority ensures the ISR network keeps the track quality high in case the damaged aircraft is lost and search-and-rescue efforts are needed. It also alerts the search-and-rescue crews to the potential for a mission or to increase their state of alert.

There are several potential benefits of a vetted, common prioritization taxonomy that should be emphasized. Most important, it supports the seamless flow of network-centric operations. Just as no ISR network can track every object within its purview all the time, neither can any single system track even a limited set of objects without errors in either tracking or ID over time. Sensors are capable of making adjustments and communicating to other sensors/systems on a microsecond timescale, orders of magnitude faster than humans operating them. For the network of systems to track, identify and maintain both track and identification on the battlespace entities as accurately and efficiently as possible, every system needs common logic to perform as operators themselves would, given the same information. Obviously, some ISR resources are allocated to finding new objects in the AOR, while others may be allocated to accumulating information on objects already found. There is a constant need to refresh data on mobile priority objects that can require coordination on a large scale between ISR assets. To eliminate most, if not all, of the competition between C2 and intelligence communities for surveillance and reconnaissance resources, common prioritization logic needs to be encoded in each system such that the sensor-to-sensor coordination can occur on that milli- or micro-second timescale.

A second benefit to aligning priorities throughout the C2 constellation is that it enables the evaluation of performance metrics at both the system and constellation level. If the constellation bandwidth were to decrease for any reason (e.g., sensors destroyed, systems jammed, etc.), then the first track quality to degrade should correspond to the target with the lowest priority, given the sensors remaining continue to cover the entire AOR.

SUMMARY

> *In today's global, information-dominated environment, effects tend to span all levels of conflict, from strategic to tactical. Simply synchronizing these effects is an incomplete approach... The U.S. military must focus on integrating its capabilities to ensure that all effects support objectives, from the lowest tactical level to the highest national level of policy.*[21]

If the entire C2 and ISR constellation works in harmony as outlined above, network-centric operations will have reached a new plateau in human-machine interface cooperation. A better term might be the human-machine partnership: machines sifting through mountains of data, separating the wheat from the chaff, with operators attending to anomalies and the "wheat" that the network finds. The coordinating logic on both sides of the interface is Commander's Intent, captured visually for the operators in a combined temporal/geo-spatial display format and captured logically for the network of systems so that they "think" like operators themselves.

No matter where an operator sits in the constellation, his or her focus should be on planning and executing successful operations that achieve the JFC's intent. As operators begin their shifts, they should readily orient themselves to the battlespace information presented. Even at "the edge," they should quickly be able to recognize battlespace priorities at any given time and make decisions that mitigate risk as a single unit, just as the commander would if he or she were everywhere at once. Based on training and experience, operators should manage resources allocated to them according to the JFC's intent and in accordance with published ROE, as translated through daily operations orders. As stated earlier, the "picture" is an approximation of truth, as best as the constellation can produce for the JFC. Based on their role and/or mission, individual operators are going to filter the common picture for information to which they need immediate or near-real-time access. So while what is displayed may change from one console to the next, the total "picture" remains common in time and space and is accessible to all (within security classification and need-to-know constraints). With that common information, both operators and networked systems alike will have the foundation from which they can meet the JFC's intent effectively and efficiently.

ENDNOTES

1   US Government, Joint Publication 3-0, *Joint Operations* (Washington, D.C., 17 September 2006), III-10.

2   David Alberts and Richard Hayes, *Power to the Edge: Command...Control...in the Information Age* (Washington, D.C.: CCRP Publication Series, 2003).

3   Department of the Army, Headquarters, Field Manual 101-5, *Staff Organization and Operations* (Washington, D.C., 31 May 1997), 1-3.

4   Field Manual 101-5, 1-3.

5   Mica Endsley, "Design and Evaluation for Situation Awareness Enhancement," *Proceedings of the Human Factors Society 32nd Annual Meeting* (Santa Monica, CA: Human Factors and Ergonomics Society, 1988), 97.

6   Lieutenant-Colonel Michael Straight, "Commander's Intent: An Aerospace Tool for Command and Control," *Airpower Journal*, 10, 1 (Spring, 1996).

7   Department of the Army, Headquarters, Field Manual 100-5, *Operations* (Washington, D.C., 14 June 1993), 6-6.

8   Carl von Clausewitz, *Vom Kriege* [*On War*] (Berlin: Ullstein, 2002).

9   Mica Endsley, "Theoretical Underpinnings of Situation Awareness: A Critical Review," in Mica Endsley and Daniel Garland, eds., *Situation Awareness Analysis and Measurement* (Mahwah, NJ: Lawrence Erlbaum Associates, 2000), 3-28.

10   Joint Publication 3-0, *Joint Operations*, III-10.

11   Robert Bolia, Todd Nelson and Michael Vidulich, "A Multi-Layer Visual Display for Air Battle Managers: Effects of Depth and Transparency on Performance and Workload in a Dual-Task Scenario," *Human Factors and Aerospace Safety* 4 (2004), 181-194. See also Harvey Smallman and Mark St. John, "Naïve Realism: Misplaced Faith in Realistic Displays," *Ergonomics in Design: The Magazine of Human Factors Applications* 13 (2005), 3.

12   Mark St. John and Glenn Osga, "Task Supervision using a Dynamic Gantt Chart Display," *Proceedings of the Human Factors and Ergonomics Society 43rd Annual Meeting* (Santa Monica, CA: Human Factors and Ergonomics Society, 1999), 168-172.

13   David Alberts, John Garstka and Frederick Stein, *Network Centric Warfare: Developing and Leveraging Information Superiority* (Washington, D.C.: CCRP, 1999), 180-181.

14   Mica Endsley, "Theoretical Underpinnings of Situation Awareness: A Critical Review," in M.R. Endsley and D.J. Garland, eds., *Situation Awareness Analysis and Measurement* (Mahwah, NJ: Lawrence Erlbaum Associates, 2000), 3-28.

15   Kevin Bennett, Michael Payne and Brett Walters, "An Evaluation of a 'Time Tunnel' Display Format for the Presentation of Temporal Information," *Human Factors* 47, 2 (2005), 342-359.

16   Joint Publication 3-0, *Joint Operations*, III-11.

17   Jeffrey Wampler, Randall Whitaker, Emilie Roth, Ronald Scott, Mona Stilson and Gina Thomas-Meyers, "Cognitive Work Aids for C2 Planning: Actionable Information to Support Operational Decision Making," *Proceedings of the 10th International Command and Control Research and Technology Symposium* (McLean, VA, June 2005).

18   Emilie Roth, Mona Stilson, Ronald Scott, Randall Whitaker, Tom Kazmierczak, Gina Thomas-Meyers and Jeffrey Wampler, "Work-centered Design and Evaluation of a C2 Visualization Aid," *Proceedings of the Human Factors and Ergonomics Society 50th Annual Meeting* (Santa Monica, CA: Human Factors and Ergonomics Society, 2005), 255-259.

19   Field Manual 101-5, 1-3.

20   For more information on this aspect, see Figure III-3 in Joint Publication 3-0, *Joint Operations*, III-12.

21   Robert Elder, "Global and Theater Operations Integration," *Joint Forces Quarterly* 46, 3 (2007), 52-54.

CONTRIBUTORS

Dr. Joseph V. Baranski is a defence scientist and head of the Collaborative Performance and Learning Section at Defence Research & Development Canada (DRDC) – Toronto. He received his PhD in cognitive psychology in 1992 from Carleton University in Ottawa, Canada. His research interests include individual and team decision-making and confidence with applications to military integrated operations, network-enabled operations, and command and control (C2).

Dr. Ann-Renée Blais is a defence scientist and member of the Collaborative Performance and Learning Section at DRDC – Toronto. She received her PhD in quantitative psychology in 2001 from Ohio State University. Her research interests include individual and cultural differences in decision-making and risk-taking, as well as quantitative methods and psychometrics.

Dr. David J. Bryant received his PhD in psychology in 1991 from Stanford University. He has conducted independent research on human spatial cognition, human factors of aviation security, and decision-making as it is related to military C2. Dr. Bryant is currently a defence scientist with DRDC – Toronto, where he is pursuing research on operational planning, inferential processes involved in situation assessment, and tactical picture compilation.

Brian Donnelly recently rejoined the Air Force Research Laboratory (AFRL) after concluding a 21-year career in the United States Air Force as a physicist, air battle manager, and program manager in C2 technology. He is currently a program manager for the Collaborative Interfaces Branch of the Human Effectiveness Directorate at AFRL. His research interests include improvements to the human-machine interface in C2 technology and defining logic in system automation.

Dr. Scott Galster received his PhD in experimental psychology from The Catholic University of America, Washington, D.C. He is a program manager for the Collaborative Interfaces for Command and Control research project at the AFRL, Wright-Patterson Air Force Base, Ohio. His research interests include human interaction with complex automated systems, tactical air battle management C2 systems, and advanced technology evaluations.

Colonel, Dr. Bernd Horn is currently the deputy commander of Canadian Special Operations Forces Command. He is an experienced infantry officer with command experience at the unit and sub-unit level. He was the commanding officer of 1st Battalion, The Royal Canadian Regiment (2001-2003); the officer commanding 3 Commando, the Canadian Airborne Regiment (1993-1995); and, the officer commanding "B" Company, 1 RCR (1992-1993). He recently served as the director of the Canadian Forces Leadership Institute (2004-2007). Colonel Horn holds an MA and PhD in war studies from the Royal Military College of Canada in Kingston, where he is an adjunct-associate professor of history. He has also authored, co-authored, edited and co-edited 20 books and numerous articles on military affairs and military history.

Sandra C. Hughes is a research psychologist in the Training and Human Performance Research & Development Branch at the Naval Air Warfare Center, Training Systems Division, in Orlando, Florida. She has conducted and/or managed research and development projects in the areas of social psychology, team performance, stress and decision-making, and distance learning design and implementation. Her recent focus has been on the social aspects of working in network-enabled operations. She received her master's degree in 1990 in industrial and organizational psychology from the University of Central Florida.

Dr. Joan Johnston is a senior research psychologist and a NAVAIR Associate Fellow at the Naval Air Warfare Center, Training Systems Division. She is responsible for managing basic, applied and advanced technology development, and prototype training research. Dr. Johnston's technical expertise is in tactical decision-making under stress, team performance and team training technologies, distributed simulation-based training, and network-enabled operations for coalition teams. She is currently the TTCP Chair of the Technical Panel 11 on The Human Aspects of Command Group. Dr. Johnston received her MA and PhD in industrial and organizational psychology from the University of South Florida.

Carol McCann heads the newly-formed Adversary Intent Section (AIS) at DRDC–Toronto. Since receiving an MASc from the University of Toronto in 1979, she has been extensively involved in investigating the human factors aspects of command and control, especially in the development of C2 concepts, systems and doctrine for the army and navy. She has carried out research in the areas of multimodal human-computer dialogue, decision support, cognitive processes in military planning, human performance under stress, and team decision making. Together with Ross Pigeau at DRDC–Toronto, she developed an influential theoretical perspective on C2 that focuses on the human as the most important component. Over the last few years, they have worked together to build an expanded research program in the social sciences at DRDC–Toronto emphasizing uniquely human aspects of C2 such as hardiness, trust, confidence, team decision-making and leadership. She has both chaired and participated in NATO and TTCP Research Study Groups on command and control. As Section Head of AIS, she will be building a research capability that will address psycho-social-cultural understanding and influence of adversary attitudes and behaviour.

Dr. Ross A. Pigeau is the director-general of DRDC–Toronto. He received both an MA and PhD in experimental psychology from Carleton University. Early in his career, Dr. Pigeau conducted research on sleep deprivation and brain electro-physiology, as well as studying vigilance fatigue among NORAD surveillance operators. In 1993, he started the Command and Control research program that emphasized such uniquely human aspects of C2 as trust, team decision-making, fatigue, leadership and common intent. Together with his colleague Carol McCann, he developed a new theoretical framework for C2, one that has influenced both Canadian military doctrine and military research and development (in Canada and internationally). He has lectured for 17 years on The Psychology of Command and Control at the Maritime Warfare Centre in Halifax, speaks regularly at the Canadian Forces College in Toronto, has contributed to the Canadian Forces profession of arms manual, *Duty With Honour*, and sits on the five-nation TTCP representing the human sciences. Dr. Pigeau became chief scientist in 2004 where he was responsible for establishing the strategic direction for human science research at DRDC – Toronto and for ensuring that high quality (and high impact) science and technology was produced. He assumed the duties of director-general during the summer of 2007.

Dr. Oshin Vartanian is a defence scientist with DRDC – Toronto. He employs cognitive science and neuroscience approaches to investigate reasoning and decision-making, especially the influence of emotions and beliefs on those processes.

GLOSSARY

3-D	Three-Dimensional
3D	Defence, Diplomacy, Development
4-D	Four-Dimensional
4GW	Fourth Generation Warfare
9/11	11 September 2001
ADF	Australian Defence Force
ADP	Army Doctrine Publications (UK)
AFRL	Air Force Research Laboratory
AIS	Adversary Intnet Section
AMC	Air Mobility Command
AOC	Air and Space Operations Center
AOI	Area of Interest
AOR	Area of Responsibility
ATD	Advanced Technology Demonstration
ATO	Air Tasking Order
AWACS	Airborne Warning and Control System
CAOC	Combined Air and Space Operations Center
C2	Command and Control
CAP	Combat Air Patrol
CCIRs	Commander's Critical Information Requirements
CDA	Canadian Defence Academy
CF	Canadian Forces
CFLI	Canadian Forces Leadership Institute
CI	Command Intent
CID	Combat Identification

ComITT	Commander's Intent Training Tool
COTS	Commercial-Off-The-Shelf
DND	Department of National Defence (Canada)
DRDC	Defence Research and Development Canada
EBAO	Effects-Based Approach to Operations
F2T2EA	Finding, Fixing, Tracking, Targeting, Engaging, Assessing
FM	Field Manual
fMRI	Functional Magnetic Resonance Imaging
HQ	Headquarters
ID	Identification
IFF	Interrogation Friend or Foe
ISR	Intelligence, Surveillance and Reconnaissance
IT	Information Technology
JFACC	Joint Force Air Component Commander
JFC	Joint Force Commander
JIMP	Joint, Interagency, Multinational, Public
MAPE	Monitor, Assess, Plan, Execute
MNE3	Multinational Experiment 3
MNE4	Multinational Experiment 4
MTMM	Multi-Trait-Multi-Method Matrix

NATO	North Atlantic Treaty Organization
NCW	Network-Centric Warfare
NEOps	Network-Enabled Operations
NGOs	Non-Governmental Organizations
NORAD	North Americal Aerospace Defense Command
NRT	Near real-time
OGDs	Other Government Departments
PPLI	Precise Position Location Information
ROEs	Rules of Engagement
ROIs	Rules of Identification
SA	Situational Awareness
SMEs	Subject Matter Experts
TACC	Tanker Airlift Control Center
TK	Tacit Knowledge
TOM	Theory of Mind
TTCP	The Technical Cooperation Panel
TTPs	Tactics, Techniques and Procedures
UK	United Kingdom
UNAMIR II	United Nations Assistance Mission for Rwanda II
US	United States
VTC	Video Teleconference

| WIDE | Work-Centered Interface Distributed Environment |
| WMDs | Weapons of Mass Destruction |

INDEX

3-D (Three Dimensional) 114, **143** *gloss.*

3D (Defence, Development and Diplomacy) 16, **143** *gloss.*

11 September 2001 (9/11) 7, **11** *notes*, **63** *notes*, **106** *notes*, **107** *notes*, **143** *gloss.*

2005 *National Defense Strategy* 112

2006 *Quadrennial Defense Review Report* 112

Action Consistency 95, 96

Advanced Technology Demonstration (ATD) 122, 123, **143** *gloss.*

Afghanistan 1, 15, **63** *notes*

Air Mobility Command (AMC) 122, 124, **143** *gloss.*

Airborne Warning and Control System (AWACS) 107, **143** *gloss.*

Al Muthanna Task Group 3

al-Qaeda 2, **11** *notes*

Anti-Goals 93, **103** *notes*

Artificial Intelligence 125

Asymmetric Strategies 2

Australia 15

Australian Army 90, **103** *notes*

Australian Defence Force (ADF) 77, **143** *gloss.*

Battle Management 113, 114, 116, 125, 140

Bernstein, Ira 29, **39** *notes*, **41** *notes*

Blogs 76

Canada i, iii, v, 1, 7, **11** *notes*, **13** *notes*, 15, 16, **38** *notes*, **39** *notes*, **42** *notes*, 45, 55, 56, 57, **83** *notes*, 87, **101** *notes*, 139, 140-142, **143** *gloss.*

Canadian Airborne Regiment 6, 140

Canadian Army 4, **38** *notes*

Canadian Forces (CF) 27, **42** *notes*, 54, 73, **83** *notes*, 87, **101** *notes*, 140, 142, **143** *gloss.*

Category-Based or Presumptive Trust 76

Cluster Analysis 34

CNN 7

Coalition Partners 3, 15, 16, 68

Cold War **11** *notes*, 106

Colquitt, J.A. 72, **83** *notes*

Combined Air & Space Operations Center (CAOC) 112, **143** *gloss.*

Command [Canadian Forces Publication 300(3)] 42, 87, **101** *notes*

Command and Control (C2) i, 16, 17, 19, 20, 22, 24, 25, 28, 32, **38-40** *notes*, **43** *notes*, **82** *notes*, **86** *notes*, 87, 94, **101-103** *notes*, 107, 109-114, 116, 120, 126, 127, 130-132, 134, 135, **136-138** *notes*, 139-142, **143** *gloss.*

Command Climate 8, 9

Command Philosophy 4, 87, 88

Commander's Critical Information Requirements (CCIRs) 119, 126, **143** *gloss.*

Commander's Intent 1, 2, 4-6, 8-10, 18, 25, 26, 51, 62, 69, **81** *notes*, 87-92, 94-100, **102-104** *notes*, 105, 106, 108-114, 117-119, 121, 125-127, 134, 135, **143** *gloss.*

Commander's Intent Statement (or Commander's Statement of Intent) 18, 26, 98, **103** *notes*

Commander's Intent Training Tool (ComITT) 97-99, **143** *gloss.*

Commander-in-Chief 112

Common Ground 27-29

Common Intent ii, 15-17, 19-33, 37, **40** *notes*, **42** *notes*, 61, 70, 74, 87, 88, 94-97, 99, **101** *notes*, **103** *notes*, 142

Communication i, iii, 2, 7, 20, 22, 24, 25, 27, 28, 33-37, **39** *notes*, **41** *notes*, 67, 74-76, **82** *notes*, **85** *notes*, 129

Competence 72-74, 76, 80

Confidence 6, 9, 36, 72, 91, 92, 139, 141

Construct Validity 17, 29-31, **39** *notes*, **41** *notes*, **42** *notes*

Contemporary Environment 1, 2

Contemporary Operating Environment vi, 1, 2, 5

Counter-Insurgency 1

Cultural Expectations 22, 23

Cyberspace 111

Darfur 15

Decision-Maker 19, 20, 23, 25, 59, 100

Decision-Making 4, 7-10, 24, 26, **40** *notes*, 60, 69, 70, 73, **81** *notes*, 87, 89, 90, 107, 108, 110, 126, 139-142

Decoupling 48, 50, 51, 62

Defence Research and Development Canada (DRDC) iii, 15, 16, 45, 87, **143** *gloss.*

Department of National Defence (DND) 7, **12** *notes*, **13** *notes*, **38** *notes*, **39** *notes*, **42** *notes*, **82** *notes*, **83** *notes*, **143** *gloss.*

Dependence 69, 74, 78-80

Distributed Teams 36, **38** *notes*, 75, 76

Distribution 75, 78-80

Diversity 35, 36, 69, 71, 76, 77-80

Dixon, Melissa 93, **103** *notes*

Edge Organization 79

Effects-Based Approach to Operations (EBAO) 16, 19, **104** *notes*, **143** *gloss.*

Effects-Based Approaches 15

Embedded Knowledge 26, **41** *notes*

Episodic Memory **63** *notes*

Explicit Intent 20-22, 36, 87, 92, 96, 100, **102** *notes*, **104** *notes*

False Belief 48-51

Farmilo, Andy 90, **102** *notes*

Farrell, Philip 94-97, 100, **103** *notes*, **104** *notes*

Folk Psychological Model of Intention 50, 51

Fong, Gwenda 93, **103** *notes*

Fourth Generation Warfare (4GW) 3, **11** *notes*, **143** *gloss.*

Free Will 45, 46, 59-63, **63** *notes*, **65** *notes*

Functional Magnetic Resonance Imaging (FMRI) 57, **144** *gloss.*

Gantt Chart 114, **136** *notes*

Geo-spatial Display 114, 116, 117, 121, 131, 134

Global War on Terror 106

Globalization 2

Groth, Lars 88, **101** *notes*

Group Dynamics Theory 79

Harvard University 3, **40** *notes*

Headline 2000 90

Hone, Geoffrey 10, 90, **102** *notes*

Hurricane Katrina 106

Identity-Based Trust 77

Ignatieff, Michael 3, **12** *notes*

Implicit Command Intent 22, 94

Implicit Intent 20-23, 26, 32, 36, 62, 87, 88, 90, 93, 94, 96, 100, **102** *notes*, **103** *notes*

Information Sharing vi, 67-69, 77, 78, 85, 88, 106

Information Technology (IT) 106, 108, 109, 127, **144** *gloss.*

Insurgency 1

Integrated Operations 3, 16, 22, 139

Intelligence, Surveillance and Reconnaissance (ISR) 113, 125, 126, 129, 130, 132-134, **144** *gloss.*

Intent Hierarchy 21

Intent Pyramid 21

Intent Transmission 88, 90, 99, 100

Intention 45-54, 56-63, **65** *notes*, 72

Internal Consistency 18, 29

Internet 2, 76, 106

Interrogation Friend or Foe (IFF) 107, **144** *gloss.*

Iraq 3, 15

Johnston, Lieutenant-General Sir Mike 67

Joint Force Air Component Commander (JFACC) 126, **144** *gloss.*

Joint Force Commander (JFC) 109, 118, 119, 125, 126, 134, 135, **144** *gloss.*

Joint, Interagency, Multinational, Public (JIMP) 16, **38** *notes*, **144** *gloss.*

Klein, Gary 93, **103** *gloss.*

Leggatt, Andrew **86** *notes*, 90, 93, 94, 100, **102-104** *notes*

LePine, J.A. 72, **83** *notes*

McCann, Carol   iii, 16, 20-25, 28, **39** *notes*, **40** *notes*, **43** *notes*, 87, 95, **101** *notes*, 141, 142

Mental Model 19, 21, 23-25, 29, 32-34, 36, **40** *notes*, **42** *notes*, 70

Middle East 77, 106

Mintzberg, Henry 88, **101** *notes*

Mission Command 4-6, 8-10, **12** *notes*, 19, **39** *notes*, 87, **101** *notes*

Molloy, Jules 97, 99, **103** *notes*, **104** *notes*

Moral Cognition 45, 46, 52, **64** *notes*

Moral Judgment 52, 53, 63

Multicultural 36, 77, 80

Multidimensional Scaling 34, **42** *notes*

Multinational Experiment 3 (MNE3) 91, **144** *gloss.*

Multinational Experiment 4 (MNE4) 95, **144** *gloss.*

Multi-Trait-Multi-Method Matrix (MTMM) 30, 31, **144** *gloss.*

Murphy, Peter 90, 91, 97, **102** *notes*, **103** *notes*

Mutual Trust 9

Network-Centric Operations **82** *notes*, 106, 108, 125, 133, 134

Network-Centric Warfare (NCW) 15, **38** *notes*, **39** *notes*, 67, 68, 70, **82** *notes*, 107, 126, 128, **137** *notes*, **144** *gloss.*

Network-Centric Warfare Maturity Model 107

Network-Enabled Operations (NEOps) 15, 19, **38** *notes*, 67-69, 71, 74, 76, 78-81, 139-141, **144** *gloss.*

New York City 7

North Atlantic Treaty Organization (NATO) **13** *notes*, 68, 141, **144** *gloss.*

New Zealand v, 15

Noble, Colonel Roger 3, **12** *notes*, **13** *notes*

Non-Governmental Organizations (NGOs) 16, **144** *gloss.*

Notional Prioritization Taxonomy 128

Nunnally, Jum 29, **39** *notes*, **41** *notes*

Office of Secretary of Defense 68

Operation Lance 6, **13** *notes*

Organizational Culture 22

Other Government Departments (OGDs) 3, 15, 16, **144** *gloss.*

Personal Expectations 21, **102** *notes*

Person-Based Trust 80

Pierce, Linda 93, **103** *notes*

Pigeau, Ross iii, 16, 20-25, 28, **39** *notes*, **40** *notes*, **43** *notes*, 87, 95, **101** *notes*, 141, 142

Power to the Edge **38** *notes*, 70, **82** *notes*, **83** *notes*, **135** *notes*

Prioritization Taxonomy 109, 125, 126, 128, 129, 133

Readiness Potential 60, 62

Reputation Scores 76

Risk Taking 71, 72, **83** *notes*

Royal Military Academy Sandhurst 99

Rules of Engagement (ROE) 128-130, 132, 134, **145** *gloss.*

Rules of Identification (ROI) 128-130, **145** *gloss.*

Scales, Major-General Robert 2, **10** *notes*

Scott, B.A. 72, **83** *notes*

Self-Synchronization 70, 107

Semantic Memory 48, **63** *notes*

Sensitivity i, 93, 94

Shared Intent 20, 33, **102** *notes*

Shattuck, Lawrence **39** *notes*, 89, 90, 97, 100, **101** *notes*

Singapore 93

Situation(al) Awareness (SA) 67, 69, 93, **103** *notes*, 107, 110, 113, 114, 116, 124, **135** *notes*, **136** *notes*, **145** *gloss.*

Social Capital 71, **83** *notes*, **84** *notes*

Social Exchange Theory 71

Social Identity Theory 76

Social Network – Interoperability 109

Socialization 22, 76

Soviet Bloc 106

Strategic Manipulation 47

Subordinate Commander's Intent 88

Suspect 128-130, 132

Swift Trust 78, 80, **85** *notes*

Tacit Knowledge (TK) 26, **40** *notes*, **41** *notes*, 92, **145** *gloss.*

Tactical Deception 47, 52

Tactics, Techniques and Procedures (TTPs) 2, **12** *notes*, **145** *gloss.*

Tanker Airlift Control Center (TACC) 122, 124, **145** *gloss.*

The Human in Command i, 21, **39** *notes*, **101** *notes*

The Technical Cooperation Panel (TTCP) v, vi, 15, 141, 142, **145** *gloss.*

Theory of Mind (TOM) 45-50, 52, 54, 59, 62, **63** *notes*, **64** *notes*, **145** *gloss.*

Thomas, Jeffrey 93, **103** *notes*

Trans-National Insurgencies 2

Trust i, 1, 4, 9, 10, 35, 57-59, **64** *notes*, 67-81, **82-86** *notes*

Two-Person Economic Exchange Game 57

Ultimatum Game 57, **64** *notes*

United Kingdom v, 15, **145** *gloss.*

United Nations Assistance Mission for Rwanda (UNAMIR) 6, **145** *gloss.*

United States (U.S.) v, **12** *notes*, 15, 16, **40** *notes*, **41** *notes*, 67-69, 77, **81** *notes*, **82** *notes*, 106, 112, 134, **145** *gloss.*

U.S. Air Force 16, 68

U.S. Army **40** *notes*, **41** *notes*

U.S. Army Field Manual (FM) 100-5 69

U.S. Joint Chiefs of Staff 67, 69

U.S. Marine Corps 91

U.S. Navy 68

U.S. Office of Force Transformation 68

U.S.-Singapore Command Experiment 93

Unity of Command 8

Video-Teleconferencing (VTC) 75, **145** *gloss.*

Weapon of Mass Destruction (WMD) 107, 127, **146** *gloss.*

Whitworth, Ian 90, **102** *notes*

Whole of Government Approach 16

Work-centered Interface Distributed Environment (WIDE) 122-124, **146** *gloss.*

World Trade Center 7

Zelibor, Rear-Admiral Thomas 68, **82** *notes*